HADLEY'S

FRENCH MEDICAL PHRASE BOOK

ENGLISH - FRENCH

by

Susan Kirkham and Alan Lindsey

HADLEY PAGER INFO

First published 2004 by Hadley Pager Info
(ISBN 1-872739-13-X)
Reprinted 2012
ISBN 978-1872739-13-7

Printed and Bound by Berforts Group, Oxford, England

HADLEY PAGER INFO,
Leatherhead, Surrey, England

CONTENTS

ABBREVIATIONS USED

f	feminine noun
m	masculine noun
pl	plural noun

Terms which are known or believed to be registered trade names or marks are designated with ®. The presence or absence of such a symbol should not be regarded as affecting the legal status of any trade mark or name.

Please note that information given here is subject to change and readers should make themselves acquainted with any recent changes in official procedures.

HOW THE HEALTH SERVICE WORKS IN FRANCE

In France, most GPs run both appointment systems and open sessions where you queue and wait. The phone numbers are in the local telephone directories in the Pages Jaunes (Yellow Pages) under the heading of Médecins: médicine générale and the name of the town or the village. Hours are also displayed outside the surgery, together with the phone number. The local mayor's office (la mairie) and Tourist Information Office (le syndicat d'initiative) will also help. Waiting times for an appointment are dependent on the surgery. It will probably take longer to get an appointment in Paris, for example, than in a small town in the country.

If you are resident in France, you will need health insurance. For the first two years after you have been working regularly in the UK and paying the National Insurance contributions, you are covered by these but need to obtain the appropriate form from the NHS Overseas Department. For this, at the time of writing, you will need the form E106, or E121 if you are of retirement age.
The address is: Department of Social Security
Pensions and Overseas Benefits Directorate
Newcastle upon Tyne
England NE98 1BA

After this, you must be a member of an insurance scheme, and will have a carte Vitale. Most treatments/consultations are reimbursable to a maximum of 70%. Top-up schemes are available to pay for the rest but these are optional. These schemes are contributory at least until you are of pensionable age. After this it will depend on your contribution record. At the doctor's you will pay for the service you have received and the money due to you will be paid at a later stage. Make sure you keep all receipts. If you are on holiday, you will need your European Health Insurance Card (EHIC), obtainable via the website **www.dh.gov.uk/travellers** or the EHIC applications telephone number 0845 606 2030. You must take this card with you in case you have any emergency medical treatment.

Out of hours treatment varies according to the locality. Some doctors cover their own emergencies, some are covered by a local duty doctor and for others you must ring the emergency number 15 which takes you through to SAMU, the paramedic service. A call to the surgery will tell you what to do and the local paper is a good source of information for Sundays and Bank Holidays (jours fériés). There is usually a page full of local information and duty cover comes under the heading Gardes de.

GPs are the first port of call for most medical needs. It is they who write prescriptions (une ordonnance) for not only drugs and treatments but also blood tests, scans, X-rays and ambulances, except where SAMU are involved. They will also write letters of referral for specialist treatment. Some doctors do the blood tests themselves but you can take the prescription to a laboratory (un laboratoire) and have it done there. Prescriptions for radiography are taken to local radiography (radiographie) centres. Ambulances are operated by local companies, who often run taxis and funeral services too!

USING FRENCH

The verbs you will need to use most often are
ÊTRE and AVOIR.

To be	Être	To have	Avoir
I am	Je suis	I have	J'ai
You are (familiar)	Tu es	You have (familiar)	Tu as
He is	Il est	He has	Il a
She is	Elle est	She has	Elle a
We are	Nous sommes	We have	Nous avons
You are	Vous êtes	You have	Vous avez
They are	Ils/elles sont	They have	Ils/elles ont

A useful phrase when you need something is: -
Je voudrais   I'd like
e.g. Je voudrais un rendez-vous   I'd like an appointment

MAKING AN APPOINTMENT
LE RENDEZ-VOUS

I should like an appointment, please	Je voudrais un rendez-vous, s'il vous plaît
It isn't urgent	Ce n'est pas urgent
It is urgent	C'est urgent
As soon as possible	Aussitôt que possible
Quarter past four next Monday	Seize heures quinze lundi prochain
At what time?	À quelle heure?

TIME

Most people in France use the 24 hour clock, thus an appointment in the afternoon would be at 16 hours (heures) and not 4 p.m. For times past or to the hour it is expressed by the hour plus the number e.g.16.10, (seize heures dix); 17.45, (dix-sept heures quarante-cinq).

[see Page 7 for Numbers, Days and Months]

USEFUL EXPRESSIONS

PHRASES UTILES

Do you speak English?	Parlez-vous anglais?
Is there anyone here who speaks English?	Est-ce qu'il y a quelqu'un qui parle anglais?
Please speak more slowly	Parlez plus lentement s'il vous plaît
I don't understand	Je ne comprends pas
What does that mean?	Qu'est-ce que ça veut dire?
What does that word mean?	Qu'est-ce que ce mot veut dire?
It is urgent	C'est urgent
It isn't urgent	Ce n'est pas urgent

MAKING AN APPOINTMENT

USEFUL EXPRESSIONS	PHRASES UTILES
As soon as possible	Aussitôt que possible
It is essential that….	Il faut absolument que….
What is the telephone number of….?	Qu'est-ce que le numéro de téléphone de….?
I'd like an appointment, please	Je voudrais un rendez-vous, s'il vous plaît
I have an appointment with/at	J'ai un rendez-vous avec/à
How much is that?	C'est combien?
I need a receipt, please	Il me faut un reçu, s'il vous plaît
How would you like to pay?	Comment voudriez-vous régler?
I'd like to pay in cash/by credit card/by cheque	Je voudrais régler en espèces/par carte bancaire/par chèque
Can I help you?	Puis-je vous aider?
Can you help me?	Est-ce que vous pouvez m'aider?
How are you?	Comment ça va?
What is the matter?	Qu'est-ce qui a?
I have a problem with….	J'ai un problème avec….
I'd like some information/ advice about….	Je voudrais des renseignements/ des conseils sur….
Can you come back tomorrow/ Monday/next week?	Vous pouvez revenir demain/ lundi/la semaine prochaine?
I need…	Il me faut…/J'ai besoin de….
What's happening?	Qu'est-ce que se passe?
Sit down	Asseyez-vous
Would you write it down	L'inscrivez, s'il vous plaît
I am looking for….	Je cherche…
I don't know	Je ne sais pas
What is your name?	Comment vous appelez-vous?
My name is….	Je m'appelle….
How is that written?	Comment ça s'inscrit?
At what time?	A quelle heure?

MAKING AN APPOINTMENT

NUMBERS. DAYS AND MONTHS

one	un, une	seventeen	dix-sept
two	deux	eighteen	dix-huit
three	trois	nineteen	dix-neuf
four	quatre	twenty	vingt
five	cinq	twenty-one	vingt-et-un
six	six	twenty-two	vingt-deux
seven	sept	twenty-three	vingt-trois
eight	huit	twenty-four	vingt-quatre
nine	neuf	twenty-five	vingt-cinq
ten	dix	thirty	trente
eleven	onze	thirty-five	trente-cinq
twelve	douze	forty	quarante
thirteen	treize	forty-five	quarante-cinq
fourteen	quatorze	fifty	cinquante
fifteen	quinze	fifty-five	cinquante-cinq
sixteen	seize		

DAYS	LES JOURS
Monday	lundi
Tuesday	mardi
Wednesday	mercredi
Thursday	jeudi
Friday	vendredi
Saturday	samedi
Sunday	dimanche

MONTHS	LES MOIS
January	janvier
February	fevrier
March	mars
April	avril
May	mai
June	juin
July	juillet
August	août
September	septembre
October	octobre
November	novembre
December	décembre

MAKING AN APPOINTMENT

GENERAL ENQUIRIES

USEFUL VOCABULARY	VOCABULAIRE UTILE
yes	oui
no	non
please	s'il vous plaît
thank you	merci
good morning	bonjour
good evening	bonsoir
goodbye	au revoir
excuse me	pardon
sorry	je m'excuse/je suis désolé/e
sir	monsieur
madam	madame
means of identification	la pièce d'identité
necessary	nécessaire
unwell	indisposé/e, souffrant/e
ill	malade
disabled	handicapé/e
serious	grave
today	aujourd'hui
tomorrow	demain
later	plus tard
next week	la semaine prochaine
last week	la semaine dernière
last night	hier soir
appointment	le rendez-vous
form	la feuille
doctor	le docteur
GP	le généraliste
dentist	le dentiste
optician	l'opticien
ophthalmologist	l'ophtalmologiste
practitioner	le praticien
specialist	le spécialiste

USEFUL VOCABULARY	VOCABULAIRE UTILE
alternative medicine	les médecines douces
surgery (place)	le cabinet
surgery (operation)	la chirurgie
medical insurance	l'assurance maladie
hospital	l'hôpital
chemist/pharmacy	la pharmacie
town centre	centre ville
toilets	les toilettes
gents	messieurs
ladies	dames
disabled toilet	handicapés
occupied	occupé
free (not occupied)	libre
free (no cost)	gratuit
closed	fermé
open	ouvert
no smoking	défense de fumer
good	bon/ne
well	bien
almost	presque
early	tôt
earlier	plus tôt
late	tard
late (to be)	en retard (être)
later	plus tard

GENERAL ENQUIRIES

VISITING THE DOCTOR'S
AU CABINET DU DOCTEUR

GENERAL HEALTH (ADULT)

Where is the doctor's surgery?	Où se trouve le cabinet du docteur?
Is there a doctor who speaks English?	Est-ce qu'il y a un docteur qui parle anglais?
Can you come to the house, please?	Vous pouvez venir à la maison, s'il vous plait?
Is there an emergency doctor at night/the weekend?	Est-ce qu'il y a un médecin de garde la nuit/le week-end?

THE DOCTOR / LE DOCTEUR

Will you take a seat in the waiting room?	Vous voulez patienter dans la salle d'attente?
How are you today?	Comment vous trouvez-vous aujourd'hui?
What is the matter?	Qu'est-ce qu'il a?
Where does it hurt?	Ça vous fait mal où?
What is your date of birth?	La date de naissance, c'est quand?
When did this happen?	Cela est arrivé quand?
How did this happen?	Comment cela est arrivé?
Get undressed please	Déshabillez-vous, s'il vous plaît
Leave on your…	Laissez votre/vos…
Take off your….	Enlevez votre/vos…
Have you lost/gained any weight recently?	Avez-vous gagné/perdu de poids récemment?
I want to weigh you	Je voudrais vous peser
Do you take any exercise?	Vous prenez de l'exercice?

THE DOCTOR	**LE DOCTEUR**
Are you on any medication?	Avez-vous des traitements en cours?
Are you allergic to...?	Êtes-vous allergique à... ?
You need a blood test	Il vous faut une prise de sang
Have you had an injection/ vaccination against...?	Vous êtes vacciné contre...?
When was your last injection/ vaccination against...?	Quelle est la date de votre dernière vaccination contre... ?
To inject/vaccinate someone against	Piquer quelqu'un contre
The stitches will need to come out in	Il faudrait enlever les sutures dans...
You need to see a specialist	Il faut consulter un spécialiste
I will refer you to my colleague	Je ferais un rendez-vous avec mon collègue
I shall give you a prescription	Je vous donnerai une ordonnance
Do you smoke?	Vous êtes fumeur?

POSSIBLE MEDICAL PROBLEMS

THE PATIENT	**LE MALADE**
I don't feel well	Je ne me sens pas bien
I'm worried because...	Je m'inquiète parce que...
I feel very weak	Je me sens très faible
I have been bitten by ...	J'ai été mordu/piqué par...
It started last night	Ça a commencé la nuit dernière
It's the first time this has happened to me	C'est la première fois que ça m'est arrivé
My...hurts/aches	Le/la...me fait mal

GENERAL HEALTH (ADULT)

THE PATIENT	LE MALADE
I have a pain in my…	J'ai mal au /à la…
It hurts when you touch it	C'est douloureux au toucher
I feel sick	J'ai mal au cœur
I feel sick	J'ai des nausées
I have/I've found a lump	J'ai/j'ai trouvé une grosseur
I have a high temperature	J'ai de la température/de la fièvre
I feel feverish	Je me sens fiévreux/fiévreuse
Can you give me something for…?	Pouvez-vous me donner quelque chose pour…?
I have a heart condition	Je suis cardiaque
I have a pacemaker	J'ai un stimulateur cardiaque
I am asthmatic	Je fais de l'asthme
I have swollen glands	J'ai des ganglions
I'm on antibiotics	Je suis sous antibiotiques
I have an inhaler	J'ai un inhalateur
I have diarrhoea	J'ai la diarrhée
I am constipated	Je suis constipé/e

SUPPORT VOCABULARY

antibiotic	antibiotique *m*
appointment	rendez-vous *m*
bill	facture *f*
bleeding	saignement *m*
blood pressure	tension *f*
blood test	prise *f* de sang
broken	cassé/e
bruise	contusion *f*
burn	brûlure *f*
burning	brûlant/e
capsule	gelule *f*

GENERAL HEALTH (ADULT)

SUPPORT VOCABULARY

clean	propre
clean (to)	nettoyer
cold (temperature)	froid/e
constipated	constipé/e
cure	remède *m*
cure (to)	guérir
cut	incision *f*
cut (to)	couper
dead	mort/e, décédé/e
diarrhoea	diarrhée *f*
dirty	sale
doctor	docteur *m*, médecin *m*
dressing	pansement *m*
examination	examen *m* medical
faint (to)	evanouir
file	dossier *m*
form	fiche *f*
furry tongue	langue *f* chargée
health/medical insurance	assurance *f* maladie
hot	chaud/e
infected	infecté/e
information	renseignements *mpl*
inhaler	inhalateur *m*
injection	injection *f*
medication	medication *f*
medicine (treatment)	medicament *f*
pay (to)	payer
pessary	pessaire *m*
pill	pilule *f*, comprimé *m*
prescription	ordonnance *f*
pulse	pouls *m*
reception	accueil *m*
rest	repos *m*
scan	échographie *f*
shiver (to)	frissonner
shock	choc *m*
sprain	entorse *f*

GENERAL HEALTH (ADULT)

SUPPORT VOCABULARY

sprain (to)	fouler (se)
sticking plaster	pansement *m* adhésif, sparadrap *m*
stitch	suture *f*
suppository	suppositoire *m*
surgery (place)	cabinet *m*
symptom	symptôme *f*
temperature	temperature *f*
test	épreuve *f*, test *m*
thermometer	thermomètre *m*
treat (to)	traiter
treatment	traitement *m*
wound	blessure *f*
x-ray	radio *f*

BABY'S HEALTH
LA SANTÉ DE BÉBÉ

DOCTOR

LE DOCTEUR

How old is baby?	Bébé a quel age?
How much does he/she weigh?	Il/elle pèse combien?
Is he/she sitting up/crawling/ walking/talking yet?	Est-ce qu'il/elle encore se tiens droit/se traîne à quatre pattes/marche/parle ?
Is he/she on solid food/weaned yet?	Est-ce qu'il/elle est encore sevré/e?
Does he/she suffer from colic/wind?	Est-ce qu'il/elle souffre de la colique?
You should apply the cream/ ointment … times a day	Il faut appliquer la crème/la pommade…fois par jour

BABY'S HEALTH

DOCTOR	**LE DOCTEUR**
Has baby been vaccinated yet?	Est-ce que bébé a encore reçu ses vaccines?
Which vaccinations has he/she been given?	Quels vaccins a-t-il/elle déjà reçu?
Put baby to sleep on his/her back	Pour coucher, installez bébé sur le dos

PARENT	**LE PARENT**
I am worried about my baby because he/she…	Je m'inquiète pour mon bébé parce qu'il/elle…
won't stop crying	pleure sans cesse
has a high temperature	a une fièvre
won't sleep	ne dort pas
is covered in a rash	a une éruption
has diarrhoea/is constipated	a la diarrhée/est constipé/e
keeps jerking up his/her knees and screaming	continue à se tortiller en hurlant
pulls his/her ear and screams	se tire l'oreille en hurlant
isn't sitting up/crawling/walking/ talking yet	ne se tiens droit/se traîne à quatre pattes/marche/parle encore
is teething	fait ses dents
is always hungry	a toujours faim
refuses to eat	refuse de manger
How much should he/she sleep?	Il lui faut combien d'heures de sommeil?
In what position should he/she sleep?	Dans quelle position il faut le/la coucher ?
Baby has nappy rash	Bébé souffre de l'érythème fessier
Baby has cradle cap	Bébé souffre des croûtes de lait

BABY'S HEALTH

PARENT	LE PARENT
How do you treat eczema?	Comment traiter l'eczéma?
When can baby start on solid food?	Quand doit-on diversifier l'alimentation?
How do I protect his/her skin from the sun?	Comment protéger la peau du soleil?

VACCINES UK	VACCINS FRANCE
BCG (early)	BCG (précoce) *m*
polio	polio *f*
diphtheria	diphtérie *f*
tetanus	tétanos *m*
pertussis (whooping cough)	coqueluche *f*
Hib (DTP+Hib)	haemophilus influenzae b *f*
men C	méningocoque C *m*
hepatitis B	hépatite B *f*
measles	rougeole *f*
mumps	oreillons *mpl*
rubella (German measles)	rubéole *f*
MMR	ROR

SUPPORT VOCABULARY

adoption	adoption *f*
allergy	allergie *f*
anaemia	anémie *f*
antibiotic	antibiotique *m*
anxiety	anxiété *f*
baby clinic	centre *m* de Protection maternelle et infantile (PMI)
bottle feed (to)	nourrir au biberon
breastfeed (to)	allaiter
breastfeeding	allaitement *m*
breastfeed on demand	tétée *f* à volunté
bottle-feed on demand	biberon *m* à volunté
bowel movement	selle *f*
burn	brûlure *f*
burp	rot *m*
catarrh	catarrhe *m*
cerebral palsy	paralysie *f* cérébrale
circumcision	circoncision *f*
cleft palate	palais fondu *m*
cold	rhume *m*
cold (to be)	avoir froid
colic	colique *f*
conjunctivitis	conjonctivite *f*
convulsion	convulsion *f*
constipation	constipation *f*
cord (umbilical)	cordon *m* (ombilical)
cot death	mort *f* subite du nourrisson
cough	toux *f*
cradle cap	croûtes *fpl* de lait
croup	croup *m*
cuddle	câlin *m*
dehydration	déshydration *f*
diarrhoea	diarrhée *f*
dirty her/his nappy (to)	émettre des selles
Down syndrome	syndrome *m* de Down

BABY'S HEALTH

SUPPORT VOCABULARY

dribble (to)	baver
dry skin	peau *f* désechée
earache	mal *m* à l'oreille
ear infection	otite *f*
eczema	eczéma *m*
fever	fièvre *f*
fontanelle	fontanelle *f*
get her/his wind up (to)	faire son rot
gum	gencive *f*
gum-soothing balm	baume gingival *m*
handicapped	handicapé/e
hare lip	bec-de-lièvre *m*
hearing problems	troubles *mpl* de l'audition
heart murmur	souffle au cœur *m*
heat stroke	coup *m* de chaleur
high temperature	forte température *f*
hiccup (to)	hoqueter
hot (to be)	avoir chaud
immunisation against	Immunisation *f* contre
impetigo	impétigo *m*
injection	injection *f*
jaundice	jaunisse *f*
maternity hospital	maternité *f*
maternity leave	congé *m* de maternité
meningitis	méningite *f*
midwife	sage-femme *f*
navel	nombril *m*
new-born baby	nouveau-né/e *m/f*
nursery nurse	puéricultrice *f*
ointment	pommade *f*
paediatrician	pédiatre *m*
pain	douleur *f*

SUPPORT VOCABULARY

paternity leave	congé *m* de paternité
pneumonia	pneumonie *f*
pulse	pouls *m*
rash	eruption *f*
regurgitate	régurgiter
respiration	respiration *f*
rickets	rachitisme *m*
scalp	cuir *m* chevalu
sight problems	troubles *mpl* de la vue
sleep through (to)	faire ses nuits
sneeze (to)	éternuer
spina bifida	spina-bifida *m*
spot	bouton *m*
sterilise	stériliser
sunburn	coup *m* de soleil
teethe (to)	faire ses dents
temperature	température *f*
tetanus	tétanos *m*
thrush	muguet *m*
toilet training	apprentissage *m* de la propreté
umbilical hernia	hernie *f* ombilicale
vaccine	vaccin *m*
virus	virus *m*
vomiting	vomissements *mpl*
wean (to)	sevrer
weigh (to)	peser
weighing	pesée *f*
whooping cough	coqueluche *f*
worms	vers *mpl*

BABY'S HEALTH

CHILDREN'S AND YOUNG PEOPLE'S HEALTH
SANTÉ DES ENFANTS ET DE LA JEUNESSE

PARENT	LE PARENT
How do I recognize the symptoms of meningitis?	Comment puis-je reconnaître les symptômes de la méningite?
I am worried about my child because he/she…	Je m'inquiète pour mon enfant parce qu'il/elle…
has had a fall	est victime d'une chute
has swallowed a…	a ingurgité un/une…
has sunstroke	a un coup de soleil
still wets the bed	fait toujours pipi au lit
is overweight	souffre de surpoids
is underweight	est maigre
has temper tantrums	fait des crises de colère
has head lice	a des poux aux cheveux
is very aggressive	est très agressif/agressive
My child has Coeliac disease	Mon enfant souffre de la maladie coeliaque
My child is allergic to…	Mon enfant est allergique …
penicillin	a la pénicilline
milk, nuts, wheat	au lait, aux noix, au blé
animal hair	aux poils des animaux
My child suffers from hay fever	Mon enfant souffre du rhume des foins
My child gets travel sick. What can I do?	Mon enfant souffre de la maladie des transports. Quoi faire?
Can you give me some information on puberty/acne/drugs/anorexia?	Pouvez-vous me donner des renseignements sur la puberté/l'acné/les drogues/l'anorexie?
My child	Mon enfant
has worms	a des vers
has a verruca. Can he/she still go swimming?	a une verrue. Il/elle peut nager encore?

PARENT	**LE PARENT**
has a problem with sleeping/ sleepwalking	a des troubles du sommeil/ somnambulisme
isn't speaking yet	tarde à parler
stammers/stutters	bégaie
can't sit still. Is he/she hyperactive?	ne tient pas en place. Est-il/elle hyperactif/hyperactive?
can't see very well	a des troubles de la vue
doesn't seem to hear properly	a l'air de ne pas entendre bien
isn't growing very fast	a des troubles de la croissance
has frequent nosebleeds	souffre des fréquentes saigne-ments de nez
I think he/she is dyslexic	je crois qu'il/elle est dyslexique
My child is asthmatic and needs an inhaler	Mon enfant est asthmatique et a besoin d'un inhalateur

SUPPORT VOCABULARY

acne	acné f
adenoids	végétations fpl
allergy	allergie f
anaphylactic shock	choc anaphylactique m
anorexia	anorexie f
antibiotic	antibiotique m
anxiety	anxiété f
appendicitis	appendicite f
asthma	asthme m
athlete's foot	mycose f
autism	autisme m
bedwetting	incontinence f nocturne

CHILDREN'S AND YOUNG PEOPLE'S HEALTH

SUPPORT VOCABULARY

burn	brûlure *f*
catarrh	catarrhe *m*
cerebral palsy	paralysie *f* cérébrale
chicken pox	varicelle *f*
circumcision	circoncision *f*
coeliac disease	maladie *f* cœliaque
cold	rhume *m*
concussion	commotion *f* cérébrale
conjunctivitis	conjonctivite *f*
cough	toux *f*
cramp	crampe *f*
dehydration	déshydration *f*
delirious	délirant
diarrhoea	diarrhée *f*
dyslexia	dyslexie *f*
ear infection	otite *f*
earache	mal *m* à l'oreille
eczema	eczéma *m*
epilepsy	épilepsie *f*
fever	fièvre *f*
food poisoning	intoxication *f* alimentaire
German measles	rubéole *f*
glandular fever	mononucléose *f* infectieuse
haemophilia	hémophilie *f*
hay fever	rhume *m* des foins
head lice	poux *mpl*
headache	mal *m* à la tête
health record	carnet *m* de santé
high temperature	forte température *f*
immunisation against	immunisation *f* contre
impetigo	impétigo *m*
inhaler	inhalateur *m*
injection	injection *f*
itch	démangeaison *f*
leukaemia	leucémie *f*

CHILDREN'S AND YOUNG PEOPLE'S HEALTH

SUPPORT VOCABULARY

measles	rougeole *f*
meningitis	méningite *f*
migraine	migraine *f*
mole	graine *f* de beauté
mumps	oreillons *mpl*
nosebleed	saignement *m* de nez
obesity	obésité *f*
pain	douleur *f*
pneumonia	pneumonie *f*
poison	poison *m*
polio	polio *f*
pulse	pouls *m*
pus	pus *m*
rash	éruption *f*
sneeze (to)	éternuer
speech impediment	troubles *mpl* du langage
speech therapy	orthophonie *f*
spina bifida	spina-bifida *m*
splinter	écharde *f*
spot	bouton *m*
stammering/stuttering	bégaiement *m*
stye	orgelet *m*
sunburn	coup de soleil *m*
temperature	température *f*
tetanus	tétanos *m*
thrush	muguet *m*
toilet training	apprentissage *m* de la propreté
tonsillitis	angine *f*
travel sickness	mal *m* des transports
tuberculosis	tuberculose *f*
urticaria	urticaire *f*
vaccine	vaccin *m*
verruca	verrue *f*
virus	virus *m*
wart	verrue *f*
whooping cough	coqueluche *f*
worms	vers *mpl*

CHILDREN'S AND YOUNG PEOPLE'S HEALTH

FEMALE HEALTH
LA SANTÉ DE FEMME

DOCTOR

What is the date of your last period?
Are you still having periods?
When was your last smear/mammography?
Do you have the previous results?
You should consult a gynaecologist

LE DOCTEUR

Quelle est la date de vos dernières règles?
Êtes-vous encore réglée?
La date de votre dernier frottis/votre dernière mammographie?
Avez-vous les résultats du dernier examen?
Il faut consulter un gynécologue

PATIENT

My periods are painful/heavy

I suffer from pre-menstrual tension
I need a smear/a mammography
When will I get the results?
I have a lump in my breast
I am having hot flushes/night sweats/mood swings

Am I starting the menopause?

I think I am anaemic
I feel tired all the time
I think I have thrush

LA MALADE

Mes règles sont douloureuses/abondantes
Je souffre du syndrome prémenstruel
Il me faut un frottis/une mammographie
Je recevrai les résultats quand?
J'ai une grosseur au sein
Je souffre des bouffées f de chaleur/sueurs f nocturnes/sautes f d'humeur
Est-ce que je suis au début de la ménopause?
Je crois que je suis anémique
Je me sens toujours fatiguée
Je crois que je souffre du muguet

PATIENT	LE MALADE
Can you give me a prescription for cystitis?	Pouvez-vous me donner une ordonnance pour la cystite?
I'd like to give up smoking	Je voudrais arrêter de fumer
I feel depressed	Je me sens dépressive
I'd like to lose weight	Je voudrais perdre des poids
Could you give me a slimming diet?	Pourriez-vous me donner un régime pour maigrir?
I am worried about AIDS	Je m'inquiète du SIDA
I had unprotected sex	J'ai eu un rapport sexuel sans contraception
I need the morning-after pill	Il me faut la contraception d'urgence
I'd like some advice on contraception	Je voudrais des conseils sur la contraception
I am pregnant	Je suis enceinte
I want an abortion	Je veux un avortement
I would like to be sterilized	Je voudrais être stérilisée

PREGNANCY AND CHILDBIRTH
LA GROSSESSE ET L'ACCOUCHEMENT

MOTHER	MAMAN
I think I am pregnant	Je crois que je suis enceinte
The test is positive/negative	Le test est positif/négatif
I'm suffering from morning sickness	Je souffre des nausées matinales
When is the baby due?	Le bébé arrivera quand?
When do I have my first antenatal check-up?	A quelle date se passera le premier entretien prénatal?

FEMALE HEALTH

MOTHER	**MAMAN**
When/where are the antenatal classes held?	Où/quand se passe les cours de préparations à l'accouchement?
I am worried that something is wrong	Je m'inquiète que tout n'aille pas bien
My husband wants to be at the birth	Mon mari voudrait assister à l'accouchement
I am having contractions	Je ressentis des contractions
I would like an epidural	Je voudrais une péridurale
I want a natural birth	Je veux un accouchement naturel
I want to push	J'ai envie de pousser
Is everything all right?	Est-ce que tout va bien?

DOCTOR	**LE DOCTEUR**
What is the date of your last period?	Quelle est la date de vos dernières règles?
You must have some blood tests	Il vous faut des examens sanguins
I need a urine sample	Il me faut un échantillon d'urine
Have you had a scan yet?	Est-ce que vous avez encore passé une échographie?
I need to give you an internal examination	Il faut vous faire un toucher vaginal
Have you felt the baby move yet?	Est-ce que vous avez encore senti bouger le bébé?
You will need a Caesarean	Il vous faudra une césarienne
I must use forceps	Il faut utiliser le forceps
Here is your son/daughter	Tenez votre fils/fille
Are you breast-feeding or bottle-feeding?	Vous allez allaiter au sein ou au biberon?

FEMALE HEALTH

SUPPORT VOCABULARY

abortion	avortement *m*, interruption *f* volontaire de grossesse (IVG)
afterbirth	placenta *m*
AIDS	SIDA *m*
amniocentesis	amniocentèse *f*
amniotic fluid	liquide *m* amniotique
ante-natal classes	cours *mpl* de préparations à l'accouchement
ante-natal clinic	clinique *f* prénatale
anaemia	anémie *f*
baby blues	coups *mpl* de blues
birthmark	naevus *m*
breaking of the waters	rupture *f* de la poche des eaux, perte *f* des eaux
breast	sein *m*
breast cancer	cancer *m* du sein
breast feed	allaiter au sein
breech	les fesses en premier
bottle feed	allaiter au biberon
Caesarian	césarienne *f*
cancer	cancer *m*
candida	candidose *f*
cervical smear	frottis *m*
cervix	col *m* de l'utérus
childbirth	accouchement *m*
chromosome	chromosome *m*
congenital	congénital
contraception	contraception *f*
condom	préservatif *m* masculin
contraceptive implant	implant *m* contraceptif
contraceptive pill	pilule *f* contraceptive
diaphragm/cap	diaphragme *m*
female condom	préservatif *m* féminin
intrauterine device	stérilet *m*
spermicides	spermicides *mpl*

FEMALE HEALTH

SUPPORT VOCABULARY

endometritis	endométrite *f*
epidural	péridurale *f*
episiotomy	épisiotomie *f*
fallopian tube	trompe *f* utérine
family planning	planification *f* familiale, planning *m* familial
fertility	fertilité *f*
fertilisation	fécondation *f*
fibroid	fibrome *m*
foetus	fœtus *m*
forceps	forceps *m*
genetic screening	test *m* de dépistage génétique
German measles	rubéole *f*
gynaecologist	gynécologue *m*
heartburn	aigreurs *fpl* de l'estomac
HIV	VIH
hot flushes	bouffées *fpl* de chaleur
hypertension	hypertension *f*
hysterectomy	hystérectomie *f*
incontinence	incontinence *f*
induce labour	déclencher l'accouchement
infertility	infertilité *f*
internal examination	toucher *m* vaginal
iron	fer *m*
labour	travail *m*
laparoscopy	laparoscopie *f*
lesbian	lesbienne *f*
mammography	mammographie *f*
mastectomy	mastectomie *f*
mastitis	mastite *f*
maternity hospital	maternité *f*
menopause	ménopause *f*
menstruation	menstruation *f*
midwife	sage-femme *f*
miscarriage	fausse couche *f*

FEMALE HEALTH

SUPPORT VOCABULARY

mood swings	sautes *fpl* d'humeur
morning sickness	nausées *fpl* matinales
mother-to-be	future maman *f*
nausea	nausée *f*
night sweats	sueurs *fpl* de nuit
nipple	mamelon *m*
obstetrician	gynécologue *m* obstétricien
oedema	œdème *m*
oestrogen	œstrogène *m*
ovary	ovaire *m*
ovulation	ovulation *f*
pain	douleur *f*
parent	parent *m*
periods	règles *fpl*
placenta	placenta *m*
pregnancy	grossesse *f*
pregnancy test	test *m* de grossesse
pregnant	enceinte
premature birth	naissance *f* prématurée, avant terme
pre-menstrual tension	syndrome *m* prémenstruel
prenatal examinations	examens *mpl* prénataux
progesterone	progestérone *f*
push (to)	pousser
relaxation	relaxation *f*, détente *f*
rhesus factor	facteur *m* rhésus
rubella	rubéole *f*
sanitary protection	protection *f* périodique
sanitary towel	serviette *f* hygiénique
scan	échographie *f*
screening	test *m* de dépistage
sexually transmitted diseases, STD	maladies *fpl* sexuellement transmissible, MST
smear	frottis *m*
speculum	spéculum *m*
sterility	stérilité *f*

FEMALE HEALTH

SUPPORT VOCABULARY

sterilization	stérilisation *f*
stitches	sutures *fpl*
tampon	tampon *m*
temperature chart	feuille *f* de température
thrush	muguet *m*
toxic shock syndrome	syndrome *m* de choc toxique
twins	jumeaux *mpl*, jumelles *fpl*
ultrasound	échographie *f*
umbilical cord	cordon *m* ombilical
uterus	utérus *m*
vagina	vagin *m*
vitamin tablet/pill	comprimé *m* de vitamine

MALE HEALTH
LA SANTÉ D'HOMME

THE PATIENT	LE MALADE
I have a problem with…	J'ai un problème avec…
I'm worried because…	Je m'inquiète à cause de…
I have found a lump	J'ai trouvé une grosseur
I am suffering from chest pains	Je souffre des douleurs de la poitrine
I want to stop smoking	Je voudrais arrêter de fumer
I'm losing my hair	Je souffre d'une chute de cheveux
I need to urinate frequently	J'ai de fréquentes envies d'uriner
I get up several times a night to urinate	Je me lève plusieurs fois la nuit pour uriner

MALE HEALTH

THE PATIENT	LE MALADE
I have trouble urinating	C'est difficile d'uriner
I have difficulty sleeping	J'ai des troubles de sommeil
I have no energy	Je manque toujours d'énergie
I always feel tired	J'ai une fatigue permanente
I have found blood in my stools	J'ai trouvé de sang dans les selles
I feel stressed/depressed	Je me sens stressé/dépressif

THE DOCTOR	LE DOCTEUR
Is there a family history of…?	Est-ce qu'il y a une histoire familiale de…?
Do you do a self-examination?	Est-ce que vous faîtes une autopalpation ?
I will show you what to do	Je vous montre quoi faire
Do you smoke/drink ?	Vous êtes fumeur/buveur ?
How many/much a day?	Combien par jour?
I must…	Il faut…
do a rectal examination	faire un toucher rectal
test your cholesterol level	faire une épreuve de votre taux de cholestérol
do a blood test	faire une prise de sang
take your blood pressure	prendre votre tension

SUPPORT VOCABULARY

acne	acné *f*
AIDS	SIDA
alcoholism	alcoolisme *m*
alopecia	alopécie *f*
anus	anus *m*
athlete's foot	mycose *f* du pied
backache	mal *m* de dos

MALE HEALTH

SUPPORT VOCABULARY

bald	chauve
cancer	cancer *m*
catheter	sonde *f*
chest pains	douleurs *fpl* de la poitrine
cholesterol	cholestérol *m*
cholesterol level	taux *m* de cholestérol
circumcision	circoncision *f*
cirrhosis (of the liver)	cirrhose *f* (du foie)
condom	préservatif *m*
contraception	contraception *f*
coronary heart disease	maladie *f* coronarienne
coronary thrombosis	infarctus *m* myocarde
dandruff	pellicules *fpl*
depression	dépression *f*
erection	érection *f*
fertility	fertilité *f*
foreskin	prépuce *m*
gay	gay *m*
genital wart	herpès *m* génital
haemophilia	hémophilie *f*
haemorrhoids	hémorroïdes *fpl*
hepatitis	hépatite *f*
hernia	hernie *f*
herpes	herpès *m*
heterosexual	hétérosexuel *m*
hiatus hernia	hernie *f* hiatale
high blood pressure	hypertension *f*
HIV	VIH
HIV negative	séronégatif/ive
HIV positive	séropositif/ive
hormone	hormone *f*
hydrocele	hydrocèle *f*
impotence	impuissance *f*
infertility	infertilité *f*

MALE HEALTH

SUPPORT VOCABULARY

itch	démangeaison
itch (to)	démanger
libido	libido *f*
male menopause	andropause *f*
muscle	muscle *m*
obesity	obésité *f*
orgasm	orgasme *m*
penis	pénis *m*
peptic ulcer	ulcère *m* duodénal
premature ejaculation	éjaculation *f* prématurée
prostate	prostate *f*
prostate gland enlargement (BPH)	adénome *m* de la prostate (HBP)
prostatectomy	prostatectomie *f*
prostatism	prostatisme *m*
prostatitis	prostatite *f*
rectal examination	toucher *m* rectal
semen	semence *f*
sexually transmitted disease STD	maladie *f* sexuellement transmissible MST
smoking (heavy)	tabagisme *m*
smoker	fumeur *m*
sperm	sperme *m*
sterility	stérilité *f*
stress	stress *m*
testicle	testicule *m*
testicular cancer	cancer *m* du testicule
testosterone	testostérone *f*
torsion of the testicles	torsion *f* testiculaire
variocele	varicocèle *f*
vasectomy	vasectomie *f*

MALE HEALTH

AT THE CHEMIST   À LA PHARMACIE

THE CUSTOMER	LE/LA CLIENT(E)
Could you prepare this prescription for me?	Pourriez-vous me préparer cette ordonnance s'il vous plaît?
Yes, it will take about 15 minutes	Bien sûr, il faudra quinze minutes pour le faire
Would you like to wait , or will you come back?	Voudriez-vous attendre ou revenir?
I will wait, thank you.	J'attendrai merci
Do you have some …	Avez-vous de l'/du…
aspirin	aspirine *f*
soluble aspirin	aspirine soluble
codeine	codéine *m*
ibuprofen	ibuprofène *m*
paracetamol	paracétamol *m*
A packet of 16 or 24?	Un paquet de 16 ou 24?
I will take the packet of 16	Je prendrai le paquet de 16
Can I get it without a prescription?	On peut l'obtenir sans ordonnance?
No it is available on prescription only	Non c'est délivré uniquement sur ordonnance
Yes it is an over-the-counter medicine	Oui c'est un médicament vendu sans ordonnance
Is this shampoo suitable for dry/ normal/ greasy hair?	Cet shampooing, est-il bon pour les cheveux seches/ normales/ grasses?
Yes, it is available in a bottle of 250 ml or 400 ml	Oui, elle est disponible en flacon de 250 ml ou de 400 ml
I'll take the bottle of 400 ml	Je prendrai le flacon de 400 ml

AT THE CHEMIST

AT THE CHEMIST   À LA PHARMACIE

THE CUSTOMER	LE/LA CLIENT(E)

I need a remedy for ...   J'ai besoin d'un remède contre…
Do you have something for ...   Avez-vous quelque chose pour..

acne	l'acné
back pain	le mal de dos
boil	un furoncle
cold	un rhume
cough	un toux
dandruff	les pellicules
diarrhoea	la diarrhée
ear infection	l'otite
flu; influenza	la grippe
hangover	une gueule de bois
headache	un mal de tête
insect bites/stings	les piqures d'insectes
mouth ulcers	les aphtes
neuralgia	la névralgie
rheumatism	le rhumatisme
sea sickness	le mal de mer
sore throat	le mal à la gorge
sprain	une entorse
upset stomach	un mal à ventre
sunburn	le coup de soleil
toothache	le mal aux dents

AT THE CHEMIST

AT THE CHEMIST   À LA PHARMACIE

TAKING MEDICINES

take the tablets	avalez les comprimés
before/after meals	avant/après les repas
in the morning/at night	le matin/le soir
with a glass of water	avec un verre d'eau
take two tablets a day after meals	prenez deux comprimés par jour après les repas
take two tea/tablespoonfuls	prenez deux cuillerées à café/à soupe

INFORMATION LEAFLETS WITH MEDICINES

LES NOTICES AVEC LES MÉDICAMENTS

ingredients	la composition
what to use it for	les indications f thérapeutiques
special precautions	les mises f en gardes spéciales
dosage	la posologie
how to take	la mode et voie d'administration
side effects	les effets non souhaités et gênants

Chemists in France are also willing and able to identify fungi for you. Simply take your fungi into the pharmacy and the person on duty will distinguish between the safe and the poisonous fungi.

AT THE CHEMIST

PHARMACY PRODUCTS

LIST OF PRODUCTS	LISTE DE PRODUITS
adhesive plaster	pansement *m* adhésif, sparadrap *m*
microporous adhesive tape	sparadrap *m* microporeux
after-sun lotion	lotion *f* après soleil
analgesic	analgésique *m*
antacid	antiacide *m*
anti-acne cream/lotion	produit *m* contre l'acné
antibiotic ointment	pommade *f* antibiotique
antidepressant	antidépresseur *m*, antidépressif *m*
antihistamine	antihistaminique *m*
antiseptic	antiseptique *m*
antiseptic cream	crème *f* antiseptique
antitussive	antitussif *m*
ascorbic acid	acide *m* ascorbique
asprin	aspirine *f*
asprin tablet	comprimé *m* d'aspirine
soluble asprin	aspirine *f* soluble
bandage	bandage *m*
elastic bandage	bandage *m* élastique
gauze bandage	bandage *m* de gaze
triangular bandage	bandage triangulaire
beta-blocker	bêta-bloquant *m*, bêta-bloqueur *m*
bleach (household)	eau *f* de Javel
boric acid	acide *m* borique
calamine	calamine *f*
calamine lotion	lotion *f* calmante à la calamine
capsule	capsule *f*
citric acid	acide *m* citrique

AT THE CHEMIST

PHARMACY PRODUCTS

codeine	codéine *f*
comb	peigne *m*
fine-tooth comb (for head lice)	peigne *m* à poux
compress	compresse *f*
compressive bandage	pansement *m* compressif
condom	préservatif *m*
contraceptive	contraceptif *m*
contraceptive pill	pilule *f* contraceptive
cortisone	cortisone *f*
cotton wool	ouate *f*, coton *m*
absorbent cotton wool	ouate *f* hydrophile
surgical cotton wool	ouate *f* chirurgicale
cotton bud	bâtonnet *m* de coton
cough lozenge/sweet	pastille *f* pour la toux
cough mixture/syrup	sirop *m* pour la toux, sirop *m* antitussif, antitussif *m*
dandruff	pellicules *fpl*
dandruff lotion	lotion *f* antipelliculaire
dandruff shampoo	shampooing *m* antipelliculaire
decongestant	décongestionnant *m*
demulcent, emollient	émollient *m*
demulcent, softener	adoucissant *m*
dental floss	fil *m* dentaire
deodorant, antiperspirant	déodorant *m*
spray/stick deodorant	déodorant *m* en spray/stick
disinfectant	désinfectant *m*, produit *m* désinfectant
disinfecting/germicidal ointment	pommade *f* anti-infection
diuretic	diurétique *m*
dressing, sterilized	compresse *f* stérilisée
dressing, bandage	pansement *m*
dressing dry/moist	pansement *m* sec/humide

AT THE CHEMIST

PHARMACY PRODUCTS

drug	drogue *f*
ear drops	gouttes *fpl* pour les oreilles
elastic support bandage	bande *f* de tissu élastique
embrocation	embrocation *f*
emetic	émétique *m*
emulsion	émulsion *f*
expectorant	expectorant *m*
eye wash/lotion	collyre *m*
eyebath	œillère *f*
eyedrops	gouttes *fpl* pour les yeux
fingerstall	doigtier *m*
first aid	premiers soins *mpl*
first aid box	trousse *f* d'urgence
first aid manual	manuel *m* de premiers soins
first aid kit	trousse *f* de premiers soins, trousse à premier secours
flannel, face flannel/cloth	gant *m* de toilette
gargle, mouthwash	gargarisme *m*
gelatine capsule	gélule *f*
ginkgo biloba	ginkgo biloba *m*
ginseng	ginseng *m*
gloves, latex/rubber	gants *mpl* latex
glucose	glucose *m*
glycerine	glycérine *f*, glycérol *m*
grain, pellet, small pill	grain *m*
healing product	cicatrisant *m*
histamine	histamine *f*
hot-water bottle	bouillotte *f*
hydrogen peroxide	eau *f* oxygénée
incontinence pad	couche *f* pour incontinents
inhaler	inhalateur *m*
mouth inhaler	inhalateur *m* buccal
pocket-size inhaler	inhalateur *m* de poche

AT THE CHEMIST

PHARMACY PRODUCTS

insect repellent	crème/lotion *f* anti-insectes
insulin	insuline *f*
laxative	laxatif *m*
lip salve	pommade *f* pour les lèvres, pommade *f* rosat
mask	masque *m*
oxygen mask	masque *m* à oxygène
mosqito repellent	produit *m* antimoustique
mouthwash	eau *f* dentifrice
nail clippers	pince *f* à ongles, coupe-ongles *m*
nailbrush	brosse *f* à ongles
nicotine patch	patch *m* à la nicotine
nose drops	gouttes *fpl* pour le nez
oil	huile *f*
almond oil	huile *f* d'amande
castor oil	huile *f* de ricin
cod liver oil	huile *f* de foie de morue
evening primrose oil	huile *f* d'onagre
olive oil	huile *f* d'olive
sunflower oil	huile *f* de tournesol
wheat germ oil	huile *f* de germe de blé
ointment for burns	pommade *f* contre les brûlures
over-the-counter medicine	médicament *m* vendu sans ordonnance
painkiller, analgesic	calmant *m* analgésique
panty liner	protège-slip *m*
paracetemol	paracétamol *m*
peroxide, hydrogen	eau *f* oxygénée
pessary	pessaire *m*, ovule *m*
pill	pilule *f*
plaster (sticking)	emplâtre *m*
corn plaster	emplâtre *m* pour les cors

AT THE CHEMIST

PHARMACY PRODUCTS

powder	poudre *f*
tooth powder	poudre *f* dentifrice
prescription	ordonnance *f*
purgative	purgation *f*, purgatif *m*, purge *f*
quinine	quinine *f*
royal jelly	gelée *f* royale
safety pin	épingle *f* de sûreté
sanitary towel	serviette *f* hygiénique
scissors	ciseaux *mpl*
sedative	sédatif *m*
sleeping pill	somnifère *m*
slimming product	produit *m* amincissant, produit *m* pour maigrir
smooth, creamy	onctueux/euse
soap	savon *m*
baby's soap	savon *m* pour bébés
dermatological soap	savon *m* dermatologique
household soap	savon *m* de Marseille
liquid soap	savon *m* liquide
mild soap	savon *m* doux
scented soap	savon *m* parfumé
shaving soap	savon *m* à barbe
soft soap	savon *m* mou
toilet soap	savon *m* de toilette
soothing cream/lotion/powder	crème *f* /lotion *f* /poudre *f* apaisante
soporific	somnifère *m*
sponge	éponge *f*
spray	spray *m*, bombe *f* aérosol
can of shaving cream	bombe *f* à raser
spray, atomizer (for inhalant, throat, nose)	vaporisateur *m*, vapo *m*
perfume atomizer	vaporisateur *m* à parfum
sterile compress	tricostéril *m*

AT THE CHEMIST

PHARMACY PRODUCTS

sterilizer	stérilisateur *m*
sterilizing solution	solution *f* de stérilisation
suntan cream	crème solaire
suntan lotion	lotion *f* solaire
suntan oil	huile *f* solaire
sun block	crème *f* écran total
tablet	comprimé *m*
aspirin tablet	comprimé *m* d'aspirine
soluble tablet	comprimé *m* soluble
chewable tablet	comprimé *m* à croquer
under-tongue tablet	comprimé *m* sublingual, linguette *f*
talc, talcum powder, baby powder	talc *m*
tampons	tampons *mpl* hygiéniques
throat pastilles	pastilles *fpl* pour la gorge
tincture, dye	teinture *f*
tincture of iodine	teinture *f* d'iode
tissues, paper handkerchiefs	mouchoirs *mpl* en papier
toilet paper	papier *m* hygiénique, papier-toilette *m*
tooth powder	poudre *f* dentifrice
toothbrush	brosse *f* à dents
toothpaste	dentifrice *m*
fluoride toothpaste	dentifrice *m* fluoré
toothpick	cure-dent *m*
tranqillizer	tranquillisant *m*, calmant *m*
tweezers	pince *f* à échardes
valerian	valériane *f*
vaseline ®	vaseline *f* ®
vitamin	vitamine *f*
with added vitamins	vitaminé
vitamin tablet/pill	comprimé *m* de vitamines
vitamin C	vitamine *f* C
wart remover	verrucide *m*
wipes	lingettes *fpl*

AT THE CHEMIST

AT THE DENTIST   CHEZ LE DENTISTE

THE PATIENT

LE MALADE

I should like an appointment, please	Je voudrais un rendez-vous, s'il vous plaît
As soon as possible	Aussitôt que possible
It is urgent	C'est urgent
I have toothache	J'ai mal aux dents
My tooth is hurting very much	La dent me fait beaucoup de douleur
I am afraid of dentists	Les dentistes me font peur
Can you stop the pain?	Vous pouvez arrêter la douleur?
Will the tooth have to come out?	Est-ce qu'il faudra enlever la dent?
Will you give me an anaesthetic?	Est-ce que vous me donnerez de l'anesthésie?
I need the toilet	J'ai besoin de la toilette
I feel sick	J'ai mal au cœur; j'ai envie de vomir
I feel faint	Je me sens évanoui/e
What treatments are available?	Qu'est-ce que le choix de traitements ?
How much will it cost?	Ça coûtera combien?
How much is that?	Ça fait combien?
I need a receipt	Il me faut un reçu
My denture is broken Can you mend it?	Le dentier s'est cassé. Pouvez-vous le réparer ?

THE DENTIST

LE DENTISTE

What is the problem?	C'est quoi, le problème ?
Can you come back later/ tomorrow?	Pouvez-vous revenir plus tard/ demain?
Sit here	Installez-vous ici
Open your mouth wide	Ouvrez bien la bouche
Rinse well	Rincez-vous bien
Don't try to swallow	N'essayez pas d'avaler

AT THE DENTIST

THE DENTIST	LE DENTISTE
Breathe slowly	Respirez lentement
Bite hard	Mordez fort
We shall have to wait a few minutes	Il faut attendre quelques moments
You need a filling	Il vous faut du plombage
I shall try to save the tooth	Je vais essayer de sauver la dent
Sorry but it will have to come out	Désolé mais il faut l'enlever
I need to take an impression for the crown/denture	Il faut prendre une impression pour la couronne/la prothèse
I need to take an X-ray	Il faut prendre une radio
Stay absolutely still	Restez absolument tranquille
You need a brace	Il vous faut un appareil orthodontique
This is only temporary. You must visit your own dentist when you get back	Ce n'est que temporaire. Il faut consulter votre propre dentiste en rentrant
I shall give you a prescription for the chemist	Je vous donnerai une ordonnance pour la pharmacie
That's all for today but I need to see you again in…	Ça va pour aujourd'hui mais il faut un rendez-vous pour…

SUPPORT VOCABULARY

abscess	abcès *m*
anaesthesia	anesthésie *f*
bacteria	bactéries *fpl*
bite to	mordre
bleeding	saignement *m*
blood test	prise de sang *f*
brace	appareil *m* orthodontique
bridge	bridge *m*

AT THE DENTIST

SUPPORT VOCABULARY

brush to	brosser
brushing	brossage *m*
caries; tooth decay	carie *m* dentaire
check-up	soins *mpl* conservation dents
chew	mastiquer
clean one's teeth to	se laver les dents
crown	couronne *f*
decay to	se carier
dental floss	fil *m* dentaire
dental health	santé *f* bucco-dentaire
dental surgery	cabinet *m* dentaire
dental technician	mécanicien-dentiste *m*
dentist	dentiste *m/f*
denture	prothèse *f* dentaire/ dentier *m*
electric toothbrush	brosse *f* à dents électrique
enamel	émail *f*
extraction	extraction *f*
filling	plombage *m*
fluoride	fluorure *m*
form	feuille *f*
gingivitis	gingivite *f*
gum	gencive *f*
halitosis/bad breath	mauvaise haleine *f*
high-speed drill	appareil *m* rotatif à grande vitesse
hypersensitive	hypersensible
inflammation	inflammation *f*
injection	injection *f*
irregular teeth	dents *fpl* mal alignées
jaw	mâchoire
look after to	soigner
milk tooth	dent *f* de lait
mouth	bouche *f*
mouthwash	bain *m* de bouche
nerve	nerf *m*
orthodontist	orthodontiste *m/f*

AT THE DENTIST

SUPPORT VOCABULARY

permanent tooth	dent *f* définitive
plaque	plaque *f* dentaire
polish	polissage *m*
prevention	prévention *f*
pyorrhea	pyorrhée *f* avéolaire
root	racine *f*
root canal	canal *m* des racines
saliva	salive *f*
scale	détartrage *m*
scan	échographie *f*
swallow to	avaler
tooth	dent *f*
toothache	mal *m* de dents
toothbrush	brosse *f* à dents
toothpaste	dentifrice *f*
ulcer	ulcère *m*
wisdom tooth	dent *f* de sagesse

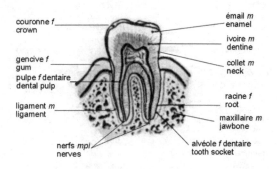

AT THE DENTIST

AT THE OPTICIAN
CHEZ L'OPTICIEN

THE OPTICIAN	L'OPTICIEN
Sit down here, please	Installez-vous par ici, s'il vous plaît
Take off your glasses	Enlevez les lunettes
I'd like a look at your glasses	Je voudrais faire un examen de vos lunettes
Do you suffer from headaches?	Est-ce que vous souffrez de maux de tête ?
I need to put some drops in your eyes	Il faut vous mettre des gouttes dans les yeux
Please wait here for a few minutes	Patientez-vous ici pendant quelques minutes
Put your chin on here	Restez le menton ici
Tell me when you see a light	Dîtes-moi quand vous voyez la lumière
What can you read?	Vous pouvez lire quoi?
Can you read this?	Vous pouvez lire ça?
How far can you read?	Vous pouvez lire jusqu'à où?
Is this better than this?	Est-ce que ça va mieux que ça?
Which is better, the first or the second?	Lequel va mieux, le premier où le deuxième?
Your eyesight has improved/ deteriorated	Votre vue s'est améliorée/ détériorée
There is a problem with…	Il y a un problème avec…
I shall give you a prescription	Je vous donnerai une ordonnance
Do you have your prescription?	Est-ce que vous avez votre ordonnance?
Would you like some new frames?	Voudriez-vous de nouvelle monture?
Are you keeping these frames?	Vous gardez la monture?
Which have you chosen?	Vous avez choisi laquelle?
They will be ready in…	Elle sera prêt…
I want to check they fit properly	Je voudrais m'assurer que tout va bien

AT THE OPTICIAN

THE PATIENT	LE MALADE
My glasses have broken. Can you mend them?	Les lunettes sont cassées. Vous pouvez les réparer?
A lens has fallen out of my glasses	Un verre s'est tombé de mes lunettes
Can you tighten the screw please?	Resserrez la vis s'il vous plaît
I need a pair of reading glasses	Il me faut des lunettes pour lire
I should like an appointment for an eye test	Je voudrais un rendez-vous pour un examen de vue
My last test was…	Le dernier examen s'est passé…
This is my last prescription	Voici ma dernière ordonnance
I suffer from headaches	Je souffre de maux de tête
I'm having sight problems	J'ai des troubles de la vue
I have difficulty seeing to read	J'ai des troubles de vue en lisant
I can only read the top line	Je ne peux lire que la première ligne
I can read as far as…	Je peux lire jusqu'à…
I have worn glasses since/for …	Je porte des lunettes depuis…
I think I need glasses	Je crois qu'il me faut de lunettes
For reading only	Seulement pour lire
I should like to try contact lenses	Je voudrais essayer de lentilles
I should like some sun glasses	Je voudrais de lunettes de soleil
How long will it take?	Il faut combien de temps ?
How much will it cost?	C'est combien?
I really like these frames	J'aime bien cette monture
I only want the lenses replacing	Il ne faut que remplacer les verres

AT THE OPTICIAN

SUPPORT VOCABULARY

antireflective	antireflet/e
astigmatism	astigmatisme *m*
bifocal	bifocal/le
blindness	cécité *f*
bridge (of the nose)	arête *f*
cataract	cataracte *f*
colour blindness	daltonisme *m*
comfortable	confortable
conjunctivitis	conjonctivite *f*
contact lens, hard/soft	lentille *f* cornéenne, dure/souple
cornea	cornée *f*
corneal graft	greffe *f* cornéenne
correction	correction *f*
cross-eyed	louché/e
detached retina	décollement *m* de la rétine
diabetes	diabète *m*
double vision	vision *f* double
drops	gouttes *fpl*
dyslexia	dyslexie *f*
eye	œil *m*
eyeball	globe *m* oculaire
eyelash	sourcil *m*
eyelid	paupière *f*
eye test	examen *m* de la vue
frames	monture *f*
glaucoma	glaucome *m*
heavy	lourd/e
inflammation f	inflammation *f*
iris	iris *m*
left	gauche
lens (of the eye)	cristallin *m*
lens (glass)	verre *m*
light (weight)	léger/ère

AT THE OPTICIAN

SUPPORT VOCABULARY

long sight	hypermétropie *f*
myopia	myopie *f*
night blindness	héméralopie *f*
nystagmus	nystagmus *m*
ophthalmologist	ophtalmologiste *m*
prescription	ordonnance *f*
read to	lire
reading glasses	lunettes *fpl* pour lire
retina	rétine *f*
right	droit/e
screw	vis *f*
shock-resistant	anti-choc
short sight	myopie *f*
squint	strabisme *m*
stye	orgelet *m*
sun glasses	lunettes *fpl* de soleil
tighten to	resserrer
uncomfortable	inconfortable, peu confortable
varifocal	progressif/ve

In France, although there are many opticians who sell glasses, few will actually do an eye test. For this you must make an appointment with an ophthalmologist (ophtalmologiste) who will examine and test your eyes then give you a prescription to take to an optician. If you are insured some of the cost will be refunded to you.

AT THE OPTICIAN

IN HOSPITAL – AS A PATIENT
À L'HÔPITAL – COMME MALADE

THE PATIENT	LE MALADE
Do you speak English?	Parlez-vous anglais?
Does anyone speak English?	Est-ce qu'il y a quelqu'un qui parle anglais?
Please speak more slowly	Parlez plus lentement, s'il vous plaît
I don't understand	Je ne comprends pas
What does that mean?	Qu'est-ce que ça veut dire?
What does that word mean?	Qu'est-ce que ce mot veut dire?
I have an appointment with/at…	J'ai un rendez-vous avec/à…
I don't have health insurance. I shall pay myself	Je n'ai pas d'assurance maladie. Je vais payer moi-même
How much is that?	C'est combien?
I need a receipt please	Il me faut un reçu, s'il vous plaît
How would you like to pay?	Comment voudriez-vous régler?
I'd like to pay in cash/by credit card/by cheque	Je voudrais régler en espèces/par carte bancaire/par chèque
I have a European Health Insurance card	J'ai une carte Européenne d'Assurance Maladie
Can I help you?	Puis-je vous aider?
Can you help me?	Est-ce que vous pouvez m'aider?
What is the matter?	Qu'est-ce qu'il y a?
I have a problem with…	J'ai un problème avec…
I'd like some information about…	Je voudrais des renseignements sur…
I need…	J'ai besoin de, il me faut
What's happening?	Qu'est-ce qui se passe?
I don't know	Je ne sais pas
What is your name?	Comment vous appelez-vous?/Votre nom ?

THE PATIENT	LE MALADE
My name is…	Je m'appelle…/Mon nom est…
What is your date of birth?	La date de naissance, c'est quand?
How are you today?	Comment ça va aujourd'hui?
What is the matter?	Qu'est-ce qu'il a?
Where does it hurt?	Où ça vous fait mal?
When did this happen?	C'est arrivé quand?
How did this happen?	Comment c'est arrivé?
I want to examine you/your …	Je voudrais faire un examen/de votre …
Get undressed please	Déshabillez-vous, s'il vous plaît
Leave on your…	Laissez votre/vos…
Take off your….	Enlevez votre/vos…
Are you on any medication?	Avez-vous des traitements en cours?
Are you allergic to…?	Êtes-vous allergique à… ?
You need a blood test	Il vous faut une prise de sang
The stitches will need to come out in ….	Il faudrait enlever les sutures dans…
I shall give you a prescription	Je vous donnerai une ordonnance
Do you smoke?	Vous êtes fumeur?
I don't feel well	Je ne me sens pas bien
I'm worried because…	Je m'inquiète parce que…
I feel very weak	Je me sens très faible
My…hurts/aches	Le/la…me fait mal
I have a pain in my…	J'ai mal au /à la…
I feel sick	J'ai mal au cœur/ J'ai des nauseas
I have/I've found a lump	J'ai/j'ai trouvé une grosseur
I have a heart condition	Je suis cardiaque
I have a pacemaker	J'ai un stimulateur cardiaque
I am asthmatic	Je fais de l'asthme

IN HOSPITAL – AS A PATIENT

THE PATIENT	LE MALADE
I'm on antibiotics	Je suis sous antibiotiques
I have an inhaler	J'ai un inhalateur
I have diarrhoea	J'ai la diarrhée
I am constipated	Je suis constipé/e
I want to go home	Je veux rentrer à la maison
I need to keep you in for observation	Il faut rester en observation
I need to operate	Il faut opérer
You can go home today/ tomorrow/in a few days	Vous pourriez rentrer aujourd'hui /demain/en quelques jours
I need to see you again next week/next month/in six months/ in a year	Il vous faut un rendez-vous pour la semaine prochaine/dans un mois/dans six mois/dans une année
I don't need to see you again	Un autre rendez-vous n'est pas nécessaire
I shall give you a letter for your GP	Je vous donnerai une lettre pour votre généraliste

SUPPORT VOCABULARY

accident and emergency	urgences *fpl*
ambulance	ambulance *f*
anaesthesia	anesthésie *f*
local	locale
general	générale
epidural	péridurale/épidurale
appointment	rendez-vous *m*
bandage	pansement *m*
bed	lit *m*
bill	facture *f*
bleeding	saignement *m*

IN HOSPITAL – AS A PATIENT

SUPPORT VOCABULARY

blood pressure	tension *f* (artérielle)
blood test	prise de sang *f*
blood transfusion	perfusion *f* sanguine
broken	cassé/e
bruise	contusion *f*
burn	brûlure *f*
capsule	gelule *f*
catheter	sonde *f*
clean	propre
clean to	nettoyer
cold (temperature)	froid/e
consulting room	cabinet *m*
coronary care	soins *mpl* coronariens
cure	remède *m*
cure to	guérir
cut	incision *f*
dead	décédé/e
dirty	sale
discharge to	renvoyer de l'hôpital
disinfect to	désinfecter
dressing	pansement *m*
drink	boisson *f*
drip	goutte à goutte *f*
examination	examen *m*
file	dossier *m*
food/meal	repas *m*
form	fiche *f*
fractured	fracturé/e
health/medical insurance	assurance *f* maladie
hot	chaud/e
infected, to be	s'infecter

IN HOSPITAL – AS A PATIENT

SUPPORT VOCABULARY

information	renseignements *mpl*
inhale	inhaler
Inhaler	inhalateur *m*
injection	injection *f*
intensive care	service *m* de réanimation
intravenous	intraveineux/euse
maternity hospital	maternité *f*
medication	médication *f*
medicine	médicament *m*
monitoring	surveillance *f*
observation	observation *f*
operation	opération *f*
oxygen	oxygène *m*
pay (to)	payer
pill	pilule *f*
pessary	pessaire *m*
plaster (for break/fracture)	plâtre *m*
plaster, adhesive (dressing)	pansement *m* adhésif
prescription	ordonnance *f*
pulse	pouls *m*
punctured	percé/e
pus	pus *m*
reception	accueil *m*
rest	repos *m*
resuscitation	réanimation *f*
shiver to	frissonner
shock	choc *m*
specimen (blood, tissue)	prélèvement *m*
specimen (urine/blood, tissue)	échantillon *m*
sprain	entorse *f*
stethoscope	stéthoscope *m*
stitch	suture *f*
suppository	suppositoire *m*
surgery (operation)	chirurgie *f*
surgery (place)	cabinet *m*

IN HOSPITAL – AS A PATIENT

SUPPORT VOCABULARY

treatment	traitement *m*
visiting hours	heures *fpl* de visite
wheelchair	fauteuil *m* roulant
wound	blessure *f*
x-ray	radio *f*, radiographie *f*

PRACTITIONERS   LES PRATICIENS

acupuncturist	acupuncteur/euse
anaesthetist	anesthésiste
aromatherapist	aromathérapiste
cardiologist	cardiologue
charge nurse	infirmier *m* en chef
chemist	pharmacien/ienne
chiropodist	pédicure
consultant	spécialiste
counsellor	conseiller/ère
dentist	dentiste
dietician	diététicien/ienne
doctor	docteur, médecin
ear, nose and throat	oto-rhino-laryngologiste
gastro-enterologist	gastro-entérologue
general practitioner - GP	généraliste
geriatrician	gérontologue
gynaecologist	gynécologue
herbalist	herboriste
homeopath	homéopathe
hospital doctor	médecin d'hôpital
nurse	infirmier/ière
occupational therapist	ergothérapeute
oncologist	oncologiste

IN HOSPITAL – AS A PATIENT

PRACTITIONERS   LES PRATICIENS

ophthalmologist	ophtalmologiste
orthopaedic	orthopédiste
paediatrician	pédiatre
paramedic	auxiliaire médical
physiotherapist	physiothérapeute
psychiatrist	psychiatre
psychologist	psychologue
radiographer	radiologue
reflexologist	réflexologiste
specialist	spécialiste
speech therapist	orthophoniste
surgeon	chirurgien/ienne
urologist	urologue

AT HOSPITAL – AS A VISITOR
À L'HÔPITAL - COMME VISITEUR

USEFUL EXPRESSIONS

PHRASES UTILES

Excuse me	Excusez-moi
Where will I find…?	Où se trouve… ?
He/she was admitted this morning/today/last night/yesterday	Il/elle est admis/e ce matin/ aujourd'hui/la nuit dernière/ hier
Where is ward…?	Où se trouve l'unité… ?
Can I use the lifts?	Puis-je prendre l'ascenseur?
What are the visiting hours?	Les heures de visite sont quand?
Can I get something to eat/to drink?	Je cherche quelque chose à manger/à boire?
Shall I come back later?	Je reviendrai plus tard?
When can he/she go home?	Il/elle pourrait rentrer à la maison quand?

USEFUL EXPRESSIONS	PHRASES UTILES
I'd like to talk to someone about it	Je voudrais le discuter avec quelqu'un
Is it serlous?	C'est grave?
Will he/she recover?	Il/elle va récupérer?
I am her/his husband/wife/mother/father/son/daughter/friend	Je suis son mari/sa femme/sa mère/son père/son fils/sa fille/ son ami/e
Can I help you?	Puis-je vous aider?
Can you help me?	Est-ce que vous pouvez m'aider?
I'd like some information about…	Je voudrais des renseignements sur…
I am looking for…	Je cherche…
Turn right/left	Tournez à droite/à gauche
Straight on	Tout droit
No smoking	Défense de fumer
I am very sorry	Je suis désolé/e
Yes	Oui
No	Non

SUPPORT VOCABULARY

A & E	urgences *fpl*
chair	chaise *f*
corridor	couloir *m*
closed	fermé
doctor	docteur *m*, médecin *m*
door	porte *f*
goodbye	au revoir
good evening	bonsoir
good morning	bonjour

AT HOSPITAL – AS A VISITOR

SUPPORT VOCABULARY

information	renseignements *mpl*
intensive care	réanimation *f*
lift, elevator	ascenseur *m*
madam	madame
numbers – odd, even	numéros – impairs, pairs
open	ouvert
please	s'il vous plaît
reception	accueil *m*
serious	grave
sir	monsieur
sorry	pardon, excusez-moi
specialist	spécialiste *m*
thank you	merci
toilets	toilettes *fpl*
gents	messieurs, hommes
ladies	femmes
disabled	handicapés
occupied	occupé
free	libre
visiting hours	heures *fpl* de visite
waiting room	salle *f* d'attente
ward	service *m*, salle *f* d'hôpital, unité *f*
maternity ward	service de *m*aternité
paediatric ward	service de pédiatrie

AT HOSPITAL – AS A VISITOR

ACCIDENTS AND EMERGENCIES
ACCIDENTS ET URGENCES

USEFUL PHRASES	DES PHRASES UTILES
Help!	Au secours!
Help me please	Aidez-moi s'il vous plaît
Does anyone speak English?	Est-ce qu'il y a quelqu'un qui parle anglais?
There has been an accident	Un accident est arrivé
There is a fire	Il y a un incendie
Watch out!	Attention!
Telephone the police/fire brigade/ambulance	Téléphonez à la police/aux pompiers/à SAMU
Do you have a mobile phone?	Est-ce que vous avez un portable?
He/she is still breathing	Il/elle est encore en vie
This is what happened	Ce qui est arrivé c'est
Is there a doctor nearby?	Est-ce qu'il y a un docteur tout près?
I have a first aid kit in the car	Il y a une trousse de premiers soins dans la voiture
He/she is unconscious	Il/elle est sans connaissance
Don't move him/her	Ne le/la bougez pas
Keep still	Tenez-vous tranquille
Do you have something to cover him/her?	Vous avez quelque chose pour le/la couvrir?
He/she is in shock	Il/elle est en un état de choc
He/she has fallen	Il/elle a fait une chute
He/she is bleeding from	Il/elle saigne du/de la
I'm ok, thank you	Je vais bien, merci
I'm not hurt	Je ne suis pas blessé/e

SUPPORT VOCABULARY

accident	accident *m*
ambulance	ambulance *f*
antiseptic wipe	lingette *f* antiseptique
bandage	pansement *m*
breathe to	respirer
broken	cassé/e
burn	brûlure *f*
car	voiture *f*
cut	coupure *f*
dead	mort/e, décédé/e
disinfectant	désinfectant *m*
doctor	docteur *m*, médecin *m*
drown (to)	se noyer
emergency	urgence *f*
emergency services	Police secours *f*
emergency ambulance services	SAMU (Service d'assistance médicale d'urgence)
faint (to)	évanouir
fall	chute *f*
fall (to)	tomber
fire	incendie *f*
fire brigade	pompiers *mpl*
first aid	premier secours *mpl*
first aid kit	trousse *f* de premiers soins
hurt oneself (to)	se faire mal
injured/wounded	blessé/e
lifebelt	bouée *f* de sauvetage
lorry	camion *m*
mobile phone	portable *m*
on fire	en flammes
elastoplast ®	pansement *m* adhésif
poison	poison *m*

ACCIDENTS AND EMERGENCIES

SUPPORT VOCABULARY	

police	police *f*
road accident	accident *m* de la route
scalded	ébouillanté/e
scissors	ciseaux *mpl*
slip to	glisser
telephone	téléphone *m*
telephone to	téléphoner
unconscious	sans connaissance

Getting Help – Emergency Numbers

These numbers may be used on a mobile phone or a land line

SAMU (Accident and Emergency)	15
Police	17
Fire Service	18
European Emergency Number	112

DEATH

In the event of a death in France, the first person to contact is a doctor. In the case of an accident, a doctor may already be present. The doctor will issue a medical certificate certifying death. In normal circumstances this serves as a burial permit. The death must be registered at the local Mairie (Town Hall). This is usually done by a member of the family, though it can also be done by the under-takers (Pompes funèbres). The undertakers should be contacted after the doctor's visit. Cremation is less common in France than

ACCIDENTS AND EMERGENCIES

in the UK though it is becoming more so. If the body is to be repatriated, the undertakers must be informed. The British Consulates will assist with making the practical arrangements. It is not obligatory to register the death of a British citizen with the British Consulate. Further information can be obtained from the consulates. Consult the local telephone directory, or the website www.amb-grandebretagne.fr

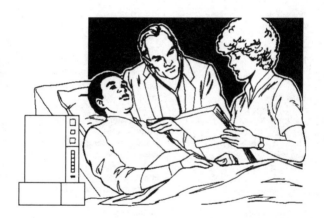

ACCIDENTS AND EMERGENCIES

REFERENCE RÉFÉRENCE

BABY'S REQUIREMENTS LES BESOINS DE BÉBÉ

absorb (to)	absorber
baby alarm	écoute-bébé f
baby bath	baignoire à bébé f
baby carrier	porte-bébé m
baby food	aliments mpl pour bébés; alimentation f pour bébé
baby lotion	lait m de toilette pour bébés
baby milk	lait m infantile
bib (baby's)	bavoir m
breast milk	lait m maternel
car seat	siège-auto m
changing mat	matelas m à langer
changing table	table f à langer
cleanser	eau f nettoyante
cot	lit m à barreaux
cotton bud	bâtonnet m à coton
dummy	sucette f
feeding bottle	biberon m
flannel/face cloth	gant m de toilette
gripe water	calmant m pour coliques
jar of baby food	petit pot m
level spoonful	cuillère f rase
level (to)	araser
mattress	matelas m
mattress cover	housse f de matelas

BABY'S REQUIREMENTS

measure	dosette *f*
nappy	couche *f*
nappy ; diaper (disposable)	couche-culotte *f*
	couche *f* en cellulose
	couche *f* jetable
nappy rash cream	crème *f* contre les rougeurs
organic	bio
plastic	plastique
plug cover	cache-prise *m*
potty	pot *m*
pushchair	poussette *f*
rubber	caoutchouc *m*
rusk	biscuit *m* pour bébés
shampoo	shampooing *m*
soap	savon *m*
spoon	cuillère *f*
stairgate	barrière *f* de sécurité
sterilize (to)	stériliser
sterilizer	stérilisateur *m*
teat (of baby's bottle)	tétine *f*
teething ring	anneau m de dentition
talcum powder	talc *m*
towel	drap *m*
toy	jouet *m*
unperfumed	sans parfum
vitamin	vitamine *f*
wipes (baby)	lingettes *fpl* de bébé

REFERENCE

COMMON ILLNESSES AND DISEASES
LES MALADIES COURANTES

abscess	abcès *m*
acne	acné *f*
addiction	dépendance *f*
alcoholism	alcoolisme *m*
allergy	allergie *f*
athlete's foot	mycose *f*
Alzheimer's disease	maladie *f* d'Alzheimer
amnesia	amnésie *f*
anaphylactic shock	choc *m* anaphylactique
anaemia	anémie *f*
aneurism	anévrisme *m*
angina	angine *f*
anorexia	anorexie *f*
anxiety	anxiété *f*
appendicitis	appendicite *f*
arthritis	arthrite *f*
asthma	asthme *m*
autism	autisme *m*
backache	mal *m* au dos
blindness	cécité *f*
bronchitis	bronchite *f*
cancer	cancer *m*
catarrh	catarrhe *m*
cerebral haemorrhage	hémorragie *f* cérébrale
cerebral palsy	paralysie *f* cérébrale
chest pains	douleurs *fpl* de poitrine
chicken pox	varicelle *f*
chill	refroidissement *m*
cirrhosis	cirrhose *f*
cleft palate	palais *m* fendu
coeliac disease	cœlialgie *f*
cold	rhume *m*

COMMON ILLNESSES AND DISEASES

cold sore	bouton de fièvre *m*
concussion	commotion *f* cérébrale
colic	colique *f*
colitis	colite *f*
colostomy	colostomie *f*
coma	coma *m*
conjunctivitis	conjonctivite *f*
constipation	constipation *f*
convulsion	convulsion *f*
coronary thrombosis	infarctus *m*
cough	toux *f*
cramp	crampe *f*
croup	croup *m*
cyst	kyste *m*
cystitis	cystite *f*
deafness	surdité *f*
dehydration	déshydration *f*
delirium	délire *f*
depression	dépression *f*
dermatitis	dermatite *f*
diabetes	diabète *m*
diarrhoea	diarrhée *f*
diphtheria	diphtérie *f*
dizziness	vertige *m*
Down's syndrome	syndrome *m* de Down
earache	mal *m* à l'oreille
ear infection	otite *f*
eczema	eczéma *m*
embolism	embolie *f*
encephalitis	encéphalite *f*
epilepsy	épilepsie *f*
fever	fièvre *f*
flatulence/wind	flatulence *f*
flu	grippe *f*
food poisoning	intoxication *f* alimentaire

REFERENCE

COMMON ILLNESSES AND DISEASES

gallstone	calcul biliaire *m*
gastroenteritis	gastro-entérite *f*
gastric ulcer	ulcère *m* de l'estomac
German measles	rubéole *f*
glandular fever	mononucléose *f* infectieuse
gout	goutte *f*
haemorrhoids	hémorroïdes *fpl*
haemorrhage	hémorragie *f*
haemophilia	hémophilie *f*
hare lip	bec de lièvre *m*
hay fever	rhume *m* des foins
headache	mal de tête *m*
heart disease	maladie de cœur *f*
heart failure	arrêt *m* du cœur
heartburn	brûlures *fpl* de l'estomac
hepatitis	hépatite *f*
hernia	hernie *f*
herpes	herpès *m*
hyperglycaemia	hyperglycémie *f*
hypoglycaemia	hypoglycémie *f*
hypertension	hypertension *f* artérielle
hyperthermia	hyperthermie *f*
impetigo	impétigo *m*
indigestion	dyspepsie *f*, indigestion *f*
influenza	grippe *f*
jaundice	jaunisse *f*
kidney stone	calcul rénal *m*
laryngitis	laryngite *f*
leukaemia	leucémie *f*
measles	rugéole *f*
melanoma	mélanome *m*
meningitis	méningite *f*
migraine	migraine *f*
multiple sclerosis	sclérose *f* en plaques
mumps	oreillons *mpl*
muscular dystrophy	dystrophie *f* musculaire

REFERENCE

COMMON ILLNESSES AND DISEASES

nausea	nausée *f*
nosebleed	saignement *m* de nez
osteoarthritis	ostéoarthrite *f*
paralysis	paralysie *f*
paraplegia	paraplégie *f*
Parkinson's disease	maladie *f* de Parkinson
peritonitis	péritonite *f*
phobia	phobie *f*
pleurisy	pleurésie *f*
pneumonia	pneumonie *f*
poisoning	empoisonnement *m*
polio	polio *f*
polyp	polype *m*
prostate cancer	cancer *m* de la prostate
pulmonary disease	maladie *f* pulmonaire
rash	éruption *f*
scabies	gale *f*
scarlet fever	scarlatine *f*
schizophrenia	schizophrénie *f*
sciatica	sciatique *f*
shock	choc *m*
sinusitis	sinusite *f*
slipped disc	hernie *f* locale
spina bifida	spina-bifida *m*
stress	stress *m*
stroke	attaque cérébrale *f*
sunburn	coup de soleil *m*
tetanus	tétanos *m*
thrombosis	thrombose *f*
thrush	muguet *m*
tinnitus	acouphène *m*
tonsillitis	angine *f*
tuberculosis	tuberculose *f*

REFERENCE

COMMON ILLNESSES AND DISEASES

ulcer	ulcère *m*
urticaria	urticaire *f*
varicose veins	varices *fpl*
vertigo	vertige *m*
virus	virus *m*
whooping cough	coqueluche *f*

THE BODY   LE CORPS

abdomen	abdomen *m*, ventre *m*
adenoids	végétations *fpl* (adénoïdes)
ankle	cheville *f*
anus	anus *m*
appendix	appendice *m*
arm	bras *m*
armpit	aisselle *f*
artery	artère *f*
ball and socket joint	joint à rotule *m*
bladder	vessie *f*
blood	sang *m*
bone	os *m*
bottom	postérieur *m*
bowel	intestins *mpl*
brain	cerveau *m*
breast	sein *m*
breastbone	sternum *m*
buttock	fesse *f*
calf	mollet *m*
cartilage	cartilage *m*
cheek	joue *f*

THE BODY

chest	poitrine *f*
chin	menton *m*
coccyx	coccyx *m*
collarbone	clavicule *f*
colon	colon *m*
ear	oreille *f*
elbow	coude *m*
eye/eyes	œil *m*/yeux *mpl*
eyebrow	sourcil *m*
eyelash	cil *m*
eyelid	paupière *f*
face	visage *m*
finger	doigt *m*
foot	pied *m*
forehead	front *m*
gallbladder	vésicule biliaire *f*
gland	glande *f*
groin	aine *f*
hand	main *f*
head	tête *f*
heart	cœur *m*
heel	talon *m*
hip	hanche *f*
intestine	intestin *m*
jaw	mâchoire *f*
joint	joint *m*
kidney	rein *m*
knee	genou *m*
kneecap	rotule *f*
larynx	larynx *m*
leg	jambe *f*
ligament	ligament *m*
lip	lèvre *f*
liver	foie *f*
lung	poumon *m*

THE BODY

midriff	diaphragme *m*
mouth	bouche *f*
muscle	muscle *m*
nail	ongle *m*
nape	nuque *f*
navel	nombril *m*
neck	cou *m*
nerve	nerf *m*
nipple	mamelon *m*
nose	nez *m*
nostril	narine *f*
oesophagus	œsophage *m*
pancreas	pancréas *m*
pelvis	bassin *m*
penis	pénis *m*
pubis	pubis *m*
rectum	rectum *m*
rib	côte *f*
ribcage	cage *f* thoracique
scrotum	scrotum *m*
shinbone	tibia *m*
shoulder	épaule *f*
shoulder blade	omoplate *f*
sinus	sinus *m*
skeleton	squelette *m*
skull	crâne *m*
spinal cord	moelle *f* épinière
spine	colonne vertébrale *f*
spleen	rate *f*
stomach	estomac *m*, ventre *m*
temple	tempe *f*
tendon	tendon *m*
thigh	cuisse *f*
thighbone	fémur *m*
thorax	thorax *m*
throat	gorge *f*

REFERENCE

THE BODY

thumb	pouce *f*
thyroid	thyroïde *f*
toe	orteil *m*
tongue	langue *f*
tonsil	tonsille *f*
tooth	dent *f*
torso	torse *m*
uterus	utérus *m*
vagina	vagin *m*
valve	valvule *f*
vein	veine *f*
vertebra	vertèbre *f*
vulva	vulve *f*
windpipe	trachée *f*
wrist	poignet *m*

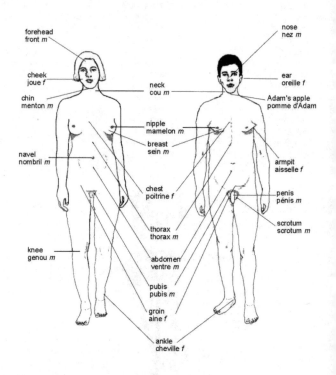

forehead
front *m*

nose
nez *m*

cheek
joue *f*

ear
oreille *f*

neck
cou *m*

chin
menton *m*

Adam's apple
pomme d'Adam

nipple
mamelon *m*

breast
sein *m*

navel
nombril *m*

armpit
aisselle *f*

chest
poitrine *f*

penis
pénis *m*

scrotum
scrotum *m*

thorax
thorax *m*

knee
genou *m*

abdomen
ventre *m*

pubis
pubis *m*

groin
aine *f*

ankle
cheville *f*

HUMAN BODY

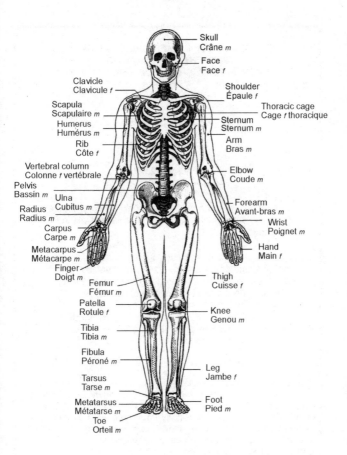

Skull
Crâne *m*

Face
Face *f*

Clavicle
Clavicule *f*

Shoulder
Épaule *f*

Scapula
Scapulaire *m*

Thoracic cage
Cage *f* thoracique

Humerus
Humérus *m*

Sternum
Sternum *m*

Rib
Côte *f*

Arm
Bras *m*

Vertebral column
Colonne *f* vertébrale

Elbow
Coude *m*

Pelvis
Bassin *m*

Ulna
Cubitus *m*

Radius
Radius *m*

Forearm
Avant-bras *m*

Carpus
Carpe *m*

Wrist
Poignet *m*

Metacarpus
Métacarpe *m*

Hand
Main *f*

Finger
Doigt *m*

Femur
Fémur *m*

Thigh
Cuisse *f*

Patella
Rotule *f*

Knee
Genou *m*

Tibia
Tibia *m*

Fibula
Péroné *m*

Tarsus
Tarse *m*

Leg
Jambe *f*

Metatarsus
Métatarse *m*

Foot
Pied *m*

Toe
Orteil *m*

SKELETON

GLOSSARY OF MEDICAL, HEALTH
AND PHARMACY TERMS
FRENCH-ENGLISH and ENGLISH-FRENCH

by Alan S. Lindsey

Paperback: 204 pages, 210 x 148 mm
Published 2003
(Reprinted 2007)
ISBN 978-1872739-12-0
Price: £12.50

> Completely new compilation providing an up-to-date source
  of over 3000 medical, health and pharmacy terms in French
  and English

> The Glossary covers a wide range of common illnesses and
  diseases, anatomical terms, first-aid and hospital terms, as
  well as pharmacy terms embracing medicines, toiletries,
  cosmetics, health and pharmaceutical products.

> Brief aide-memoire definitions in French and English of
  numerous medical terms. Many phrases (French and English)
  for usage in a medical situation.

The above publication is available through good booksellers or can
be obtained directly from Hadley Pager Info by sending a cheque to
cover the price (postage is free within the UK, add 10% if in Europe,
or 16% if outside Europe) **to Hadley Pager Info, PO Box 249,
Leatherhead, KT23 3WX, England**. Latest Publication List also
available from this address, or visit our Website at
http://www.hadleypager.com

HADLEY'S

GUIDE ANGLAIS DE PHRASES MÉDICALES

FRANÇAIS – ANGLAIS

par

Susan Kirkham et Alan Lindsey

HADLEY PAGER INFO

First published 2004 by Hadley Pager Info
(ISBN 1-872739-13-X)
(Reprinted 2012)
ISBN 978-1872739-13-7

Printed and Bound by Berforts Group, Oxford, England

HADLEY PAGER INFO,
Leatherhead, Surrey, England

TABLE DES MATIÈRES

ABRÉVIATIONS UTILISÉES

f   nom féminin
m   nom masculin
pl   nom au pluriel

Les termes qui sont connus ou crus d'être les marques déposées sont signalés par le symbole ®. Cependant la présence ou l'absence de ce symbole ne constitue nullement une indication quant à la valeur juridique de ces termes.

COMMENT FONCTIONNENT LES SERVICES MÉDICAUX DU ROYAUME-UNI

Pour tous les ressortissants de l'Union Européen, les soins délivrés par le NHS (le service public de la santé du Royaume-Uni) sont gratuits.

Si vous partez en vacances, étudier ou étes detaché par votre employeur au Royaume-Uni il faut procurer La Carte Européenne d'Assurance Maladie (ce n'est pas la même chose comme la carte Vitale). Pour obtenir votre carte, adressez-vous à votre caisse d'Assurance Maladie au moins deux semaines avant votre départ.

Chez le medicin, le pharmacien et dans les hôpitaux du service public presenter votre Carte Européenne d'Assurance Maladie. Grâce à votre carte vos frais médicaux sont pris en charge dans les mêmes conditions que pour les assurés du Royaumes-Uni.

D'habitude il faut faire un rendez-vous avec un généraliste (GP) à son cabinet (surgery) mais il existe des centres médicaux où on faut simplement arriver et attendre un docteur. Ils s'appellent les drop-in centres. La plupart des résidents sont enregistrés chez un généraliste.

En cas d'urgence, allez directement à l'hôpital au service des urgences (Casualty, A&E, Accident and Emergency).

Le traitement en hôpital est gratuit, même s'il faut y rester.

Par contre il ne reste pas beaucoup de dentistes qui travaillent pour le service public. Il y a des drop-in centres mais le traitement n'est pas gratuit.

Si vous prenez de médicament, c'est toujours utile de porter une liste des médicaments en partant pour l'étranger.

UTILISANT ANGLAIS

Les verbes qu'il vous faudra le plus souvent sont TO BE and TO HAVE

Être	To be	Avoir	To have
Je suis	I am	J'ai	I have
Tu es	You are (familiar)	Tu as	You have (familiar)
Il est	He is	Il a	He has
Elle est	She is	Elle a	She has
Nous sommes	We are	Nous avons	We have
Vous êtes	You are	Vous avez	You have
Ils/elles sont	They are	Ils/elles ont	They have

Quand il vous faut quelque chose, une phrase utile est :-

I'd like   Je voudrais

e.g. I'd like an appointment   Je voudrais un rendez-vous

LE RENDEZ-VOUS

Je voudrais un rendez-vous, s'il vous plaît	I should like an appointment, please
Ce n'est pas urgent	It isn't urgent
C'est urgent	It is urgent
Aussitôt que possible	As soon as possible
Seize heures quinze lundi prochain	Quarter past four next Monday

L'HEURE

En le Royaume-Uni, le plupart des gens n'utilise que les nombres 1 à 12 pour dire l'heure. Donc il faut préciser, par exemple, si c'est six heures du matin ou du soir.

[voir page 87 pour les nombres, les jours, et les mois]

PHRASES UTILES

USEFUL PHRASES

Parlez-vous français?	Do you speak French?
Est-ce qu'il y a quelqu'un qui parle français?	Is there anyone here who speaks French?
Parlez plus lentement s'il vous plaît	Please speak more slowly
Je ne comprends pas	I don't understand
Qu'est-ce que ça veut dire?	What does that mean?
Qu'est-ce que ce mot veut dire?	What does that word mean?
Il faut absolument que….	It is essential that….
Qu'est-ce que le numéro de téléphone de….?	What is the telephone number of….?
Je voudrais un rendez-vous, s'il vous plaît	I'd like an appointment, please

LE RENDEZ-VOUS

LE RENDEZ-VOUS

PHRASES UTILES	USEFUL PHRASES
J'ai un rendez-vous avec/à	I have an appointment with/at
C'est combien?	How much is that?
Il me faut un reçu, s'il vous plaît	I need a receipt, please
Comment voudriez-vous régler?	How would you like to pay?
Je voudrais régler en espèces /par carte bancaire/par chèque	I'd like to pay in cash/by credit card/by cheque
Puis-je vous aider?	Can I help you?
Est-ce que vous pouvez m'aider?	Can you help me?
Comment ça va?	How are you?
Qu'est-ce qui a?	What is the matter?
J'ai un problème avec….	I have a problem with….
Je voudrais des renseigne-ments/des conseils sur….	I'd like some information/advice about….
Vous pouvez revenir demain/ lundi/la semaine prochaine?	Can you come back tomorrow/ Monday/next week?
Il me faut…/J'ai besoin de…	I need…
Qu'est-ce que se passe?	What's happening?
Asseyez-vous	Sit down
L'inscrivez, s'il vous plaît	Would you write it down
Je cherche…	I am looking for….
Je ne sais pas	I don't know
Comment vous appelez-vous?	What is your name?
Je m'appelle….	My name is….
Comment ça s'inscrit?	How is that written?
A quelle heure?	At what time?

LE RENDEZ-VOUS

LES NOMBRES. LES JOURS ET LES MOIS

un, une	one	dix-sept	seventeen
deux	two	dix-huit	eighteen
trois	three	dix-neuf	nineteen
quatre	four	vingt	twenty
cinq	five	vingt-et-un	twenty-one
six	six	vingt-deux	twenty-two
sept	seven	vingt-trois	twenty-three
huit	eight	vingt-quatre	twenty-four
neuf	nine	vingt-cinq	twenty-five
dix	ten	trente	thirty
onze	eleven	trente-cinq	thirty-five
douze	twelve	quarante	forty
treize	thirteen	quarante-cinq	forty-five
quatorze	fourteen	cinquante	fifty
quinze	fifteen	cinquante-cinq	fifty-five
seize	sixteen		

LES JOURS	DAYS
lundi	Monday
mardi	Tuesday
mercredi	Wednesday
jeudi	Thursday
vendredi	Friday
samedi	Saturday
dimanche	Sunday

LES MOIS	MONTHS
janvier	January
fevrier	February
mars	March
avril	April
mai	May
juin	June
juillet	July
août	August
septembre	September
octobre	October
novembre	November
décembre	December

LE RENDEZ-VOUS

SE RENSEIGNER

PHRASES UTILES	USEFUL PHRASES
oui	yes
non	no
s'il vous plaît	please
merci	thank you
bonjour	good morning
bonsoir	good evening
au revoir	goodbye
pardon	excuse me
je m'excuse/je suis désolé/e	sorry
monsieur	sir
madame	madam
la pièce d'identité	means of identification
nécessaire	necessary
indisposé/e, souffrant/e	unwell
malade	ill
handicapé/e	disabled
grave	serious
aujourd'hui	today
demain	tomorrow
plus tard	later
la semaine prochaine	next week
la semaine dernière	last week
hier soir	last night
le rendez-vous	appointment
la feuille	form
le docteur	doctor
le généraliste	GP
le dentiste	dentist
l'opticien	optician
l'ophtalmologiste	ophthalmologist
le praticien	practitioner
le spécialiste	specialist

SE RENSEIGNER

PHRASES UTILES	USEFUL PHRASES
les médecines douces	alternative medicine
le cabinet	surgery (place)
la chirurgie	surgery (operation)
l'assurance maladie	medical insurance
l'hôpital	hospital
la pharmacie	chemist/pharmacy
centre ville	town centre
les toilettes	toilets
messieurs	gents
dames	ladies
handicapés	disabled toilet
occupé	occupied
libre	free (not occupied)
gratuit	free (no cost)
fermé	closed
ouvert	open
défense de fumer	no smoking
bon/ne	good
bien	well
presque	almost
tôt	early
plus tôt	earlier
tard	late
en retard (être)	late (to be)
plus tard	later

AU CABINET DU DOCTEUR
VISITING THE DOCTOR'S

SANTÉ GÉNÉRALE (ADULTE)

Où se trouve le cabinet du docteur?	Where is the doctor's surgery?
Est-ce qu'il y a un docteur qui parle français?	Is there a doctor who speaks French?
Vous pouvez venir à la maison, s'il vous plaît?	Can you come to the house, please?
Est-ce qu'il y a un médecin de garde la nuit/le week-end?	Is there an emergency doctor at night/the weekend?

LE DOCTEUR / THE DOCTOR

Vous voulez patienter dans la salle d'attente?	Will you take a seat in the waiting room?
Comment vous trouvez-vous aujourd'hui?	How are you today?
Qu'est-ce qu'il a?	What is the matter?
Ça vous fait mal où?	Where does it hurt?
La date de naissance, c'est quand?	What is your date of birth?
Cela est arrivé quand?	When did this happen?
Comment cela est arrivé?	How did this happen?
Déshabillez-vous, s'il vous plaît	Get undressed please
Laissez votre/vos…	Leave on your…
Enlevez votre/vos…	Take off your….
Avez-vous gagné/perdu de poids récemment?	Have you lost/gained any weight recently?
Je voudrais vous peser	I want to weigh you

SANTÉ GÉNÉRALE (ADULTE)

LE DOCTEUR	THE DOCTOR
Vous prenez de l'exercice?	Do you take any exercise?
Avez-vous des traitements en cours?	Are you on any medication?
Êtes-vous allergique à… ?	Are you allergic to…?
Il vous faut une prise de sang	You need a blood test
Vous êtes vacciné contre…?	Have you had an injection/ vaccination against…?
Quelle est la date de votre dernière vaccination contre… ?	When was your last injection/ vaccination against…?
Piquer à quelqu'un contre	To inject/vaccinate someone against
Il faudrait enlever les sutures dans…	The stitches will need to come out in ….
Il faut consulter un spécialiste	You need to see a specialist
Je ferais un rendez-vous avec mon collègue	I will refer you to my colleague
Je vous donnerai une ordonnance	I shall give you a prescription
Je suis allergique à l'aspirine	I am allergic to aspirin
Je suis allergique à la pénicilline	I am allergic to penicillin
Vous êtes fumeur?	Do you smoke?

PROBLÈMES MÉDICAUX POSSIBLES

LE MALADE	THE PATIENT
Je ne me sens pas bien	I don't feel well
Je m'inquiète parce que…	I'm worried because…
Je me sens très faible	I feel very weak

SANTÉ GÉNÉRALE (ADULTE)

LE MALADE	THE PATIENT
J'ai été mordu/piqué par…	I have been bitten by …
Ça a commencé la nuit dernière	It started last night
C'est la première fois que ça m'arrive	It's the first time this has happened to me
Le/la…me fait mal	My…hurts/aches
J'ai mal au /à la…	I have a pain in my…
C'est douloureux au toucher	It hurts when you touch it
J'ai mal au cœur	I feel sick
J'ai des nauseas	I feel sick
J'ai/j'ai trouvé une grosseur	I have/I've found a lump
J'ai de la temperature/de la fièvre	I have a high temperature
Je me sens fiévreux/fiévreuse	I feel feverish
Pouvez-vous me donner quelque chose pour…?	Can you give me something for…?
Je suis cardiaque	I have a heart condition
J'ai un stimulateur cardiaque	I have a pacemaker
Je fais de l'asthme	I am asthmatic
J'ai des ganglions	I have swollen glands
Je suis sous antibiotiques	I'm on antibiotics
J'ai un inhalateur	I have an inhaler
J'ai la diarrhée	I have diarrhoea
Je suis constipé/e	I am constipated

VOCABULAIRE SUPPLÉMENTAIRE

accueil *m*	reception
antibiotique *m*	antibiotic
assurance *f* maladie	health/medical insurance
blessure *f*	wound
brûlant/e	burning
brûlure *f*	burn

SANTÉ GÉNÉRALE (ADULTE)

VOCABULAIRE SUPPLÉMENTAIRE

cabinet *m*	surgery (place)
cassé/e	broken
chaud/e	hot
choc *m*	shock
constipé/e	constipated
contusion *f*	bruise
couper	cut (to)
diarrhée *f*	diarrhoea
dossier *m*	file
échographie *f*	scan
entorse *f*	sprain
épreuve *f*, test *m*	test
évanouir	faint (to)
examen *m* medical	examination
facture *f*	bill
fiche *f*	form
fouler (se)	sprain (to)
frissonner	shiver (to)
froid/e	cold
gelule *f*	capsule
guérir	cure (to)
incision *f*	cut
infecté/e	infected
injection *f*	injection
langue *f* chargée	furry tongue
medicament *f*	medicine (treatment)
medication *f*	medication
nettoyer	clean (to)
ordonnance *f*	prescription
pansement *m*	dressing
pansement *m* adhésif, sparadrap *m*	sticking plaster
payer	pay (to)

SANTÉ GÉNÉRALE (ADULTE)

VOCABULAIRE SUPPLÉMENTAIRE

pessaire *m*	pessary
pilule *f*, comprimé *m*	pill
pouls *m*	pulse
prise *f* de sang	blood test
propre	clean
radio *f*	x-ray
remède *m*	cure
rendez-vous *m*	appointment
renseignements *mpl*	information
repos *m*	rest
saignement *m*	bleeding
sale	dirty
suppositoire *m*	suppository
suture *f*	stitch
symptôme *f*	symptom
tension *f*	blood pressure
traitement *m*	treatment
traiter	treat (to)

SANTÉ GÉNÉRALE (ADULTE)

LA SANTÉ DE BÉBÉ   BABY'S HEALTH

LE DOCTEUR

DOCTOR

Bébé a quel age?

How old is baby?

Il/elle pèse combien?

How much does he/she weigh?

Est-ce qu'il/elle encore se tiens droit/se traîne à quatre pattes/ marche/parle?

Is he/she sitting up/ crawling/walking/talking yet?

Est-ce qu'il/elle est encore sevré/e?

Is he/she on solid food/weaned yet?

Est-ce qu'il/elle souffre de la colique?

Does he/she suffer from colic/ wind?

Il faut appliquer la crème/la pommade…fois par jour

You should apply the cream/ ointment … times a day

Est-ce que bébé a encore reçu ses vaccins ?

Has baby been vaccinated yet?

Quels vaccins a-t-il/elle déjà reçu?

Which vaccinations has he/she been given?

Pour coucher, installez bébé sur le dos

Put baby to sleep on her/his back

LE PARENT

PARENT

Je m'inquiète pour mon bébé parce qu'il/elle…

I am worried about my baby because he/she…

pleure sans cesse

won't stop crying

a une fièvre

has a high temperature

ne dort pas

won't sleep

a une éruption

is covered in a rash

a la diarrhée/est constipé/e

has diarrhoea/is constipated

continue à se tortiller en hurlant

keeps jerking up his/her knees and screaming

se tire l'oreille en hurlant

pulls his/her ear and screams

ne se tiens droit/se traîne à quatre pattes/marche/parle encore

isn't sitting up/ crawling/ walking/ talking yet

LA SANTÉ DE BÉBÉ

LA SANTÉ DE BÉBÉ

LE PARENT	PARENT
fait ses dents	is teething
a toujours faim	is always hungry
refuse de manger	refuses to eat
Il lui faut combien d'heures de sommeil?	How much should he/she sleep?
Dans quelle position il faut la/le coucher?	In what position should he/she sleep?
Bébé souffre de l'érythème fessier	Baby has nappy rash
Bébé souffre des croûtes de lait	Baby has cradle cap
Comment traiter l'eczéma?	How do you treat eczema?
Quand doit-on diversifier l'alimentation?	When can baby start on solid food?
Comment protéger la peau du soleil?	How do I protect her/his skin from the sun?

VACCINS (FRANCE)	VACCINES (UK)
BCG (précoce) *m*	BCG (early)
polio *f*	polio
diphtérie *f*	diphtheria
tétanos *m*	tetanus
coqueluche *f*	pertussis (whooping cough)
haemophilus influenzae b *f*	hib (DTP+Hib)
méningocoque C *m*	men C
hépatite B *f*	hepatitis B
rougeole *f*	measles
oreillons *mpl*	mumps
rubéole *f*	rubella (German measles)
ROR *m*	MMR

VOCABULAIRE SUPPLÉMENTAIRE

adoption *f*	adoption
allaitement *m*	breastfeeding
allaiter	breastfeed (to)
allergie *f*	allergy
anémie *f*	anaemia
antibiotique *m*	antibiotic
anxiété *f*	anxiety
apprentissage *m* de la propreté	toilet training
avoir chaud	hot (to be)
avoir froid	cold (to be)
baume gingival *m*	gum-soothing balm
baver	dribble (to)
bec-de-lièvre *m*	hare lip
biberon *m* à volonté	bottle-feed on demand
bouton *m*	spot
brûlure *f*	burn
câlin *m*	cuddle
catarrhe *m*	catarrh
centre *m* de protection maternelle et infantile (PMI)	baby clinic
circoncision *f*	circumcision
colique *f*	colic
congé *m* de maternité	maternity leave
congé *m* de paternité	paternity leave
conjonctivite *f*	conjunctivitis
constipation *f*	constipation
convulsion *f*	convulsion
coqueluche *f*	whooping cough
cordon *m* (ombilical)	cord (umbilical)
coup *m* de chaleur	heat stroke
coup *m* de soleil	sunburn
croup *m*	croup
croûtes *fpl* de lait	cradle cap

LA SANTÉ DE BÉBÉ

VOCABULAIRE SUPPLÉMENTAIRE

cuir *m* chevalu	scalp
déshydration *f*	dehydration
diarrhée *f*	diarrhoea
douleur *f*	pain
eczéma *m*	eczema
émettre des selles	dirty her/his nappy (to)
éruption *f*	rash
éternuer	sneeze (to)
faire ses dents	teethe (to)
faire ses nuits	sleep through (to)
faire son rot	get her/his wind up (to)
fièvre *f*	fever
fontanelle *f*	fontanelle
forte température *f*	high temperature
gencive *f*	gum
handicapé/e	handicapped
hernie *f* ombilicale	umbilical hernia
hoqueter	hiccup (to)
immunisation *f* contre	immunization against
impétigo *m*	impetigo
injection *f*	injection
jaunisse *f*	jaundice
mal *m* à l'oreille	earache
maternité *f*	maternity hospital
méningite *f*	meningitis
mort *f* subite du nourrisson	cot death
muguet *m*	thrush
nombril *m*	navel
nourrir au biberon	bottle feed (to)
nouveau-né/e *m* /*f*	new-born baby
otite *f*	ear infection
palais fondu *m*	cleft palate
paralysie *f* cérébrale	cerebral palsy

LA SANTÉ DE BÉBÉ

VOCABULAIRE SUPPLÉMENTAIRE

peau *f* désechée	dry skin
pédiatre *m*	paediatrician
pesée *f*	weighing
peser	weigh (to)
pneumonie *f*	pneumonia
pommade *f*	ointment
pouls *m*	pulse
puéricultrice *f*	nursery nurse
rachitisme *m*	rickets
régurgiter	regurgitate
respiration *f*	respiration
rhume *m*	cold
rot *m*	burp
sage-femme *f*	midwife
selle *f*	bowel movement
sevrer	wean (to)
souffle au cœur *m*	heart murmur
spina-bifida *m*	spina bifida
stériliser	sterilise
syndrome *m* de Down	Down syndrome
température *f*	temperature
tétanos *m*	tetanus
tétée *f* à volunté	breastfeed on demand
toux *f*	cough
troubles *mpl* de l'audition	hearing problems
troubles *mpl* de la vue	sight problems
vaccin *m*	vaccine
vers *mpl*	worms
virus *m*	virus
vomissements *mpl*	vomiting

LA SANTÉ DE BÉBÉ

LA SANTÉ DES ENFANTS ET DE LA JEUNESSE
CHILDREN'S AND YOUNG PEOPLE'S HEALTH

LE PARENT

PARENT

Comment puis-je reconnaître les symptômes de la méningite?	How do I recognize the symptoms of meningitis?
Je m'inquiète pour mon enfant parce qu'il/elle…	I am worried about my child because he/she…
est victime d'une chute	has had a fall
a ingurgité un/une…	has swallowed a…
a un coup de soleil	has sunstroke
fait toujours pipi au lit	still wets the bed
souffre de surpoids	is overweight
est maigre	is underweight
fait des crises de colère	has temper tantrums
a des poux aux cheveux	has head lice
est très agressif/agressive	is very aggressive
a des vers	has worms
a une verrue. Il/elle peut nager encore?	has a verruca. Can he/she still go swimming?
a des troubles du sommeil/ somnambulisme	has a problem with sleeping/ sleepwalking
tarde à parler	isn't speaking yet
bégaie	stammers/stutters
ne tient pas en place. Est-il/elle hyperactive?	can't sit still. Is he/she hyperactive?
a des troubles de la vue	can't see very well
a l'air de ne pas entendre bien	doesn't seem to hear properly
a des troubles de la croissance	isn't growing very fast
souffre des fréquentes saignements de nez	has frequent nosebleeds
Je crois qu'il/elle est dyslexique	I think he/she is dyslexic
Mon enfant est asthmatique et a besoin d'un inhalateur	My child is asthmatic and needs an inhaler

LA SANTÉ DES ENFANTS ET DE LA JEUNESSE

LE PARENT	PARENT
Mon enfant souffre de la maladie cœliaque	My child has Coeliac disease
Mon enfant est allergique …	My child is allergic to …
à la pénicilline	penicillin
au lait, aux noix, au blé	milk, nuts, wheat
aux poils des animaux	animal hair
Mon enfant souffre du rhume des foins	My child suffers from hay fever
Mon enfant souffre de la maladie des transports. Quoi faire?	My child gets travel sick. What can I do?
Pouvez-vous me donner des renseignements sur la puberté/ l'acné/les drogues/l'anorexie?	Can you give me some information on puberty/ acne/drugs/anorexia?

VOCABULAIRE SUPPLÉMENTAIRE

acné *f*	acne
allergie *f*	allergy
angine *f*	tonsillitis
anorexie *f*	anorexia
antibiotique *m*	antibiotic
anxiété *f*	anxiety
appendicite *f*	appendicitis
apprentissage *m* de la propreté	toilet training
asthme *m*	asthma
autisme *m*	autism
bégaiement *m*	stammering/stuttering
bouton *m*	spot
brûlure *f*	burn
carnet *m* de santé	health record
catarrhe *m*	catarrh

LA SANTÉ DES ENFANTS ET DE LA JEUNESSE

VOCABULAIRE SUPPLÉMENTAIRE

choc anaphylactique *m*	anaphylactic shock
circoncision *f*	circumcision
commotion *f* cérébrale	concussion
conjonctivite *f*	conjunctivitis
coqueluche *f*	whooping cough
coup de soleil *m*	sunburn
crampe *f*	cramp
délirant	delirious
démangeaison *f*	itch
déshydration *f*	dehydration
diarrhée *f*	diarrhoea
douleur *f*	pain
dyslexie *f*	dyslexia
écharde *f*	splinter
eczéma *m*	eczema
épilepsie *f*	epilepsy
éruption *f*	rash
éternuer	sneeze (to)
fièvre *f*	fever
forte température *f*	high temperature
graine *f* de beauté	mole
hémophilie *f*	haemophilia
immunisation *f* contre	immunisation against
impétigo *m*	impetigo
incontinence *f* nocturne	bedwetting
inhalateur *m*	inhaler
injection *f*	injection
intoxication *f* alimentaire	food poisoning
leucémie *f*	leukaemia
mal *m* à l'oreille	earache
mal *m* à la tête	headache
mal *m* des transports	travel sickness
maladie *f* cœliaque	Coeliac disease
méningite *f*	meningitis

LA SANTÉ DES ENFANTS ET DE LA JEUNESSE

VOCABULAIRE SUPPLÉMENTAIRE

migraine *f*	migraine
mononucléose *f* infectieuse	glandular fever
muguet *m*	thrush
mycose *f*	athlete's foot
obésité *f*	obesity
oreillons *mpl*	mumps
orgelet *m*	stye
orthophonie *f*	speech therapy
otite *f*	ear infection
paralysie *f* cérébrale	cerebral palsy
pneumonie *f*	pneumonia
poison *m*	poison
polio *f*	polio
pouls *m*	pulse
poux *mpl*	head lice
pus *m*	pus
rhume *m*	cold
rhume *m* des foins	hay fever
rougeole *f*	measles
rubéole *f*	German measles
saignement *m* de nez	nosebleed
spina-bifida *m*	spina bifida
température *f*	temperature
tétanos *m*	tetanus
toux *f*	cough
troubles *mpl* du langage	speech impediment
tuberculose *f*	tuberculosis
urticaire *f*	urticaria
vaccin *m*	vaccine
varicelle *f*	chicken pox
végétations *fpl*	adenoids
verrue *f*	verruca
verrue *f*	wart
vers *mpl*	worms
virus *m*	virus

LA SANTÉ DES ENFANTS ET DE LA JEUNESSE

LA SANTÉ DE FEMME
FEMALE HEALTH

LE DOCTEUR

Quelle est la date de vos dernières règles?
Êtes-vous encore réglée?
La date de votre denier frottis/ votre dernière mammographie?
Avez-vous les résultats du dernier examen?
Il faut consulter un gynécologue

DOCTOR

What is the date of your last period?
Are you still having periods?
When was your last smear/ mammography?
Do you have the previous results?
You should consult a gynaecologist

LA MALADE

Mes règles sont douloureuses/ abondantes
Je souffre du syndrome prémenstruel
Il me faut un frottis/une mammographie
Je recevrai les résultats quand?
J'ai une grosseur au sein
Je souffre des bouffées f de chaleur/sueurs f nocturnes/ sautes f d'humeur
Est-ce que je suis au début de la ménopause?
Je crois que je suis anémique
Je me sens toujours fatiguée
Je crois que je souffre du muguet

PATIENT

My periods are painful/heavy

I suffer from pre-menstrual tension
I need a smear/a mammography

When will I get the results?
I have a lump in my breast
I am having hot flushes/night sweats/mood swings

Am I starting the menopause?

I think I am anaemic
I feel tired all the time
I think I have thrush

LA SANTÉ DE FEMME

LA MALADE	PATIENT
Pouvez-vous me donner une ordonnance pour la cystite?	Can you give me a prescription for cystitis?
Je voudrais arrêter de fumer	I'd like to give up smoking
Je me sens dépressive	I feel depressed
Je voudrais perdre des poids	I'd like to lose weight
Pourriez-vous me donner un régime pour maigrir?	Could you give me a slimming diet?
Je m'inquiète du SIDA	I am worried about AIDS
J'ai eu un rapport sexuel sans contraception	I had unprotected sex
Il me faut la contraception d'urgence	I need the morning-after pill
Je voudrais des conseils sur la contraception	I'd like some advice on contraception
Je suis enceinte	I am pregnant
Je veux un avortement	I want an abortion
Je voudrais être stérilisée	I would like to be sterilized

LA GROSSESSE ET L'ACCOUCHEMENT
PREGNANCY AND CHILDBIRTH

MAMAN	MOTHER
Je crois que je suis enceinte	I think I am pregnant
Le test est positif/négatif	The test is positive/negative
Je souffre des nausées matinales	I'm suffering from morning sickness
Le bébé arrivera quand?	When is the baby due?
A quelle date se passera le premier entretien prénatal?	When do I have my first antenatal check-up?
Où/quand se passe les cours de préparations à l'accouchement?	When/where are the antenatal classes held?
Je m'inquiète que tout n'aille pas bien	I am worried that something is wrong

LA SANTÉ DE FEMME

LA SANTÉ DE FEMME

MAMAN

Mon mari voudrait assister à
  l'accouchement
Je ressentis des contractions
Je voudrais une péridurale
Je veux un accouchement
  naturel
J'ai envie de pousser
Est-ce que tout va bien?

MOTHER

My husband wants to be at the
  birth
I am having contractions
I would like an epidural
I want a natural birth

I want to push
Is everything all right?

LE DOCTEUR

Quelle est la date de vos
  dernières règles?
Il vous faut des examens
  sanguins
Il me faut un échantillon d'urine
Est-ce que vous avez encore
  passé une échographie?
Il faut vous faire un toucher
  vaginal
Est-ce que vous avez encore
  senti bouger le bébé?
Il vous faudra une césarienne
Il faut utiliser le forceps
Tenez votre fils/fille
Vous allez allaiter au sein ou au
  biberon?

DOCTOR

What is the date of your last
  period?
You must have some blood tests

I need a urine sample
Have you had a scan yet?

I need to give you an internal
  examination
Have you felt the baby move
  yet?
You will need a Caesarean
I must use forceps
Here is your son/daughter
Are you breast-feeding or bottle-
  feeding?

VOCABULAIRE SUPPLÉMENTAIRE

accouchement *m*	childbirth
aigreurs *fpl* de l'estomac	heartburn
allaiter au biberon	bottle feed
allaiter au sein	breast feed
amniocentèse *f*	amniocentesis
anémie *f*	anaemia
avortement *m* /interruption *f* volontaire de grossesse (IVG)	abortion
bouffées *fpl* de chaleur	hot flushes
cancer *m*	cancer
cancer *m* du sein	breast cancer
candidose *f*	candida
césarienne *f*	Caesarian
chromosome *m*	chromosome
clinique prénatale *f*	ante-natal clinic
col *m* de l'utérus	cervix
comprimé *m* de vitamine	vitamin pill/tablet
congénital	congenital
contraception *f*	contraception
préservatif *m* masculin	condom
implant *m* contraceptif	contraceptive implant
pilule *f* contraceptive	contraceptive pill
diaphragme *m*	diaphragm/cap
préservatif *m* féminin	female condom
stérilet *m*	intrauterine device
spermicides *mpl*	spermicides
cordon *m* ombilical	umbilical cord
coups *m* pl de blues	baby blues
cours *mpl* de préparations à l'accouchement	ante-natal classes
cystite *f*	cystitis
déclencher l'accouchement	induce labour
dilatation *f* et curettage	dilatation and curettage (D&C)

LA SANTÉ DE FEMME

VOCABULAIRE SUPPLÉMENTAIRE

douleur *f*	pain
échographie *f*	scan
échographie *f*	ultrasound
éclampsie *f*	eclampsia
embryon *m*	embryo
enceinte	pregnant
endométrite *f*	endometritis
épisiotomie *f*	episiotomy
examens *mpl* prénataux	prenatal examinations
facteur *m* rhésus	rhesus factor
fausse couche *f*	miscarriage
fécondation *f*	fertilisation
fer *m*	iron
fertilité *f*	fertility
fesses *fpl* en premier	breech
feuille *f* de température	temperature chart
fibrome *m*	fibroid
fœtus *m*	foetus
forceps *m*	forceps
frottis *m*	cervical smear
future maman *f*	mother-to-be
grossesse *f*	pregnancy
grossesse *f* extra-utérine	ectopic pregnancy
gynécologue *m*	gynaecologist
gynécologue *m* obstétricien	obstetrician
hypertension *f*	hypertension
hystérectomie *f*	hysterectomy
incontinence *f*	incontinence
infertilité *f*	infertility
jumeaux *mpl*/ jumelles *fpl*	twins
kyste *m*	cyst
laparoscopie *f*	laparoscopy
liquide *m* amniotique	amniotic fluid

LA SANTÉ DE FEMME

VOCABULAIRE SUPPLÉMENTAIRE

maladies *fpl* sexuellement transmissible, MST	sexually transmitted diseases, STD
mamelon *m*	nipple
mammographie *f*	mammography
mastectomie *f*	mastectomy
mastite *f*	mastitis
maternité *f*	maternity hospital
ménopause *f*	menopause
menstruation *f*	menstruation
muguet *m*	thrush
naevus *m*	birthmark
naissance *f* prématurée/avant terme	premature birth
nausée *f*	nausea
nausées *fpl* matinales	morning sickness
œdème *m*	oedema
œstrogène *m*	oestrogen
ouverture *f* du col	dilation
ovaire *m*	ovary
ovulation *f*	ovulation
parent *m*	parent
péridurale *f*	epidural
placenta *m*	placenta, afterbirth
planification *f* familiale/planning *m* familial	family planning
pousser	push (to)
progestérone *f*	progesterone
protection *f* périodique	sanitary protection
règles *fpl*	periods
relaxation *f*/détente *f*	relaxation
rubéole *f*	German measles, rubella
rupture *f* de la poche des eaux/ perte *f* des eaux	breaking of the waters

LA SANTÉ DE FEMME

VOCABULAIRE SUPPLÉMENTAIRE

sage-femme *f*	midwife
sautes *fpl* d'humeur	mood swings
sein *m*	breast
serviette *f* hygiénique	sanitary towel
SIDA *m*	AIDS
spéculum *m*	speculum
stérilisation *f*	sterilization
stérilité *f*	sterility
sueurs *fpl* de nuit	night sweats
sutures *fpl*	stitches
syndrome *m* de choc toxique	toxic shock syndrome
syndrome *m* prémenstruel	pre-menstrual tension
tampon *m*	tampon
test *m* de dépistage	screening
test *m* de dépistage génétique	genetic screening
test *m* de grossesse	pregnancy test
toucher *m* vaginal	internal examination
travail *m*	labour
trompe *f* utérine	fallopian tube
utérus *m*	uterus
vagin *m*	vagina
VIH	HIV

LA SANTÉ DE FEMME

LA SANTÉ D'HOMME   MALE HEALTH

LE MALADE

J'ai un problème avec…	I have a problem with…
Je m'inquiète à cause de…	I'm worried because…
J'ai trouvé une grosseur	I have found a lump
Je souffre des douleurs de la poitrine	I am suffering from chest pains
Je voudrais arrêter de fumer	I want to stop smoking
Je souffre d'une chute de cheveux	I'm losing my hair
J'ai de fréquentes envies d'uriner	I need to urinate frequently
Je me lève plusieurs fois la nuit pour uriner	I get up several times a night to urinate
C'est difficile d'uriner	I have trouble urinating
J'ai des troubles de sommeil	I have difficulty sleeping
Je manque toujours d'énergie	I have no energy
J'ai une fatigue permanente	I always feel tired
J'ai trouvé de sang dans les selles	I have found blood in my stools
Je me sens stressé/dépressif	I feel stressed/depressed

THE PATIENT

LE DOCTEUR

Est-ce qu'il y a une histoire familiale de…?	Is there a family history of…?
Est-ce que vous faîtes une autopalpation?	Do you do a self-examination?
Je vous montrerai quoi faire	I will show you what to do
Vous êtes fumeur/buveur?	Do you smoke/drink?
Combien par jour?	How many/much a day?
Il faut…	I must…
faire un toucher rectal	do a rectal examination

THE DOCTOR

LA SANTÉ D'HOMME

LA SANTÉ D'HOMME   MALE HEALTH

LE DOCTEUR	**THE DOCTOR**
faire une épreuve de votre taux de cholestérol	test your cholesterol level
faire une prise de sang	do a blood test
prendre votre tension	take your blood pressure

VOCABULAIRE SUPPLÉMENTAIRE

acné *f*	acne
adénome *m* de la prostate (HBP)	prostate gland enlargement (BPH)
alcoolisme *m*	alcoholism
alopécie *f*	alopecia
andropause *f*	male menopause
anus *m*	anus
cancer *m*	cancer
cancer *m* du testicule	testicular cancer
chauve	bald
cholestérol *m*	cholesterol
circoncision *f*	circumcision
cirrhose *f* (du foie)	cirrhosis (of the liver)
contraception *f*	contraception
démangeaison *f*	itch
démanger	itch to
dépression *f*	depression
douleurs *fpl* de la poitrine	chest pains
éjaculation *f* prématurée	premature ejaculation
érection *f*	erection
fertilité *f*	fertility
fumeur *m*	smoker
gay *m*	gay

VOCABULAIRE SUPPLÉMENTAIRE

hémophilie *f*	haemophilia
hémorroïdes *fpl*	haemorrhoids
hépatite *f*	hepatitis
hernie *f*	hernia
hernie *f* hiatale	hiatus hernia
herpès *m*	herpes
herpès *m* génital	genital wart
hétérosexuel *m*	heterosexual
hormone *f*	hormone
hydrocèle *f*	hydrocele
hypertension *f*	high blood pressure
impuissance *f*	impotence
infarctus *m* myocarde	coronary thrombosis
infertilité *f*	infertility
libido *f*	libido
mal *m* de dos	backache
maladie *f* coronarienne	coronary heart disease
maladie *f* sexuellement transmissible MST	sexually transmitted disease STD
muscle *m*	muscle
mycose *f* du pied	athlete's foot
obésité *f*	obesity
orgasme *m*	orgasm
pellicules *fpl*	dandruff
pénis *m*	penis
prépuce *m*	foreskin
préservatif *m*	condom
prostate *f*	prostate
prostatectomie *f*	prostatectomy
prostatisme *m*	prostatism
prostatite *f*	prostatitis
semence *f*	semen
séronégatif/ive	HIV negative
séropositif/ive	HIV positive

LA SANTÉ D'HOMME

VOCABULAIRE SUPPLÉMENTAIRE

SIDA	AIDS
sonde *f*	catheter
sperme *m*	sperm
stérilité *f*	sterility
stress *m*	stress
tabagisme *m*	smoking (heavy)
taux *m* de cholestérol	cholesterol level
testicule *m*	testicle
testostérone *f*	testosterone
torsion *f* testiculaire	torsion of the testicles
toucher *m* rectal	rectal examination
ulcère *m* duodénal	peptic ulcer
varicocèle *f*	variocele
vasectomie *f*	vasectomy
VIH	HIV

LA SANTÉ D'HOMME

À LA PHARMACIE   AT THE CHEMIST

LE/LA CLIENT(E)	THE CUSTOMER
Pourriez-vous me préparer cette ordonnance s'il vous plaît?	Could you prepare this prescription for me?
Bien sûr, il faudra quinze minutes pour la faire	Yes, it will take about 15 minutes
Voudriez-vous attendre ou revenir?	Would you like to wait , or will you come back?
J'attendrai merci	I will wait, thank you.
Vous avez de l'/du......?	Do you have some ......?
aspirine *f*	aspirin
aspirine soluble	soluble aspirin
codéine *m*	codeine
ibuprofène *m*	ibuprofen
paracétamol *m*	paracetamol
Un paquet de 16 ou 24?	A packet of 16 or 24?
Je prendrai le paquet de 16	I will take the packet of 16
Puis-je l'obtenir sans ordonnance?	Can I get it without a prescription?
Non c'est délivré uniquement sur ordonnance	No it is available on prescription only
Oui c'est un médicament vendu sans ordonnance	Yes it is an over-the-counter medicine
Cet shampooing, est-il bon pour les cheveux seches/ normales/grasses?	Is this shampoo suitable for dry/ normal/ greasy hair?
Oui, elle est disponible en flacon de 250 ml ou de 400 ml	Yes, it is available in a bottle of 250 ml or 400 ml
Je prendrai le flacon de 400 ml	I'll take the bottle of 400 ml

À LA PHARMACIE

LE/LA CLIENT(E)	THE CUSTOMER
J'ai besoin d'un remède contre ..	I need a remedy for ....
Avez-vous quelque chose pour ..	Do you have something for ....

l'acné	acne
les aphtes	mouth ulcers
le coup de soleil	sunburn
la diarrhée	diarrhoea
une entorse	sprain
un furoncle	boil
la grippe	flu; influenza
une gueule de bois	hangover
le mal aux dents	toothache
le mal de dos	back pain
le mal à la gorge	sore throat
le mal de mer	sea sickness
un mal de tête	headache
un mal à ventre	upset stomach
l'otite	ear infection
la névralgie	neuralgia
les pellicules	dandruff
les piqures d'insectes	insect bites/stings
le rhumatisme	rheumatism
un rhume	cold
un toux	cough

LES NOTICES AVEC LES MÉDICAMENTS — INFORMATION LEAFLETS WITH MEDICINES

la composition	ingredients
les indications *f* thérapeutiques	what to use it for
les mises *f* en gardes spéciales	special precautions
la posologie	dosage
la mode et voie d'administration	how to take
effets non souhaités et gênants	side effects

À LA PHARMACIE

PRODUITS DE PHARMACIE

LISTE DE PRODUITS	LIST OF PRODUCTS
acide *m* ascorbique	ascorbic acid
acide *m* borique	boric acid
acide *m* citrique	citric acid
adoucissant *m*	demulcent, softener
analgésique *m*	analgesic
antiacide *m*	antacid
antidépresseur *m* antidé- pressif *m*	antidepressant
antihistaminique *m*	antihistamine
antiseptique *m*	antiseptic
antitussif *m*	antitussive
aspirine *f*	asprin
bandage *m*	bandage
bandage *m* élastique	elastic bandage
bandage *m* de gaze	gauze bandage
bandage triangulaire	triangular bandage
bande *f* de tissu élastique	elastic support bandage
bêta-bloquant *m*	beta-blocker
bêta-bloqueur *m*	
bouillotte *f*	hot-water bottle
brosse *f* à dents	toothbrush
brosse *f* à ongles	nailbrush
calamine *f*	calamine
calmant *m* analgésique	painkiller, analgesic
capsule *f*	capsule
cicatrisant *m*	healing product
ciseaux *mpl*	scissors
codéine *f*	codeine
collyre *m*	eye wash/lotion
compresse *f*	compress
compresse *f* stérilisée	dressing, sterilized

À LA PHARMACIE

PRODUITS DE PHARMACIE

comprimé *m*	tablet
comprimé *m* d'aspirine	aspirin tablet
comprimé *m* soluble	soluble tablet
comprimé *m* à croquer	chewable tablet
comprimé *m* sublingual, linguette *f*	under-tongue tablet
contraceptif m	contraceptive
cortisone *f*	cortisone
couche *f* pour incontinents	incontinence pad
crème *f* /lotion *f* /poudre *f* apaisante	soothing cream/lotion/powder
crème *f* antiseptique	antiseptic cream
crème *f* écran total	sun block
crème solaire	suntan cream
lotion *f* solaire	suntan lotion
huile *f* solaire	suntan oil
crème/lotion *f* anti-insectes	insect repellent
cure-dent *m*	toothpick
décongestionnant *m*	decongestant
dentifrice *m*	toothpaste
dentifrice *m* fluoré	fluoride toothpaste
déodorant *m*	deodorant, antiperspirant
déodorant *m* en spray	spray deodorant
déodorant *m* en stick	stick deodorant
désinfectant *m* , produit *m* désinfectant	disinfectant
diurétique *m*	diuretic
doigtier *m*	fingerstall
drogue *f*	drug
eau *f* de Javel	bleach (household)
eau *f* dentifrice	mouthwash
eau *f* oxygénée	hydrogen peroxide
eau *f* oxygénée	peroxide, hydrogen

À LA PHARMACIE

PRODUITS DE PHARMACIE

embrocation *f*	embrocation
émétique *m*	emetic
émollient *m*	demulcent, emollient
emplâtre *m*	plaster (sticking)
emplâtre *m* pour les cors	corn plaster
émulsion *f*	emulsion
épingle *f* de sûreté	safety pin
éponge *f*	sponge
expectorant *m*	expectorant
fil *m* dentaire	dental floss
gant *m* de toilette	flannel, face flannel/cloth
gants *mpl* latex	gloves, latex/rubber
gargarisme *m*	gargle, mouthwash
gelée *f* royale	royal jelly
gélule *f*	gelatine capsule
ginkgo biloba *m*	ginkgo biloba
ginseng *m*	ginseng
glucose *m*	glucose
glycérine *f*, glycérol *m*	glycerine
gouttes *fpl* pour le nez	nose drops
gouttes *fpl* pour les oreilles	ear drops
gouttes *fpl* pour les yeux	eyedrops
grain *m*	grain, pellet, small pill
histamine *f*	histamine
huile *f*	oil
huile *f* d'amande	almond oil
huile *f* de ricin	castor oil
huile *f* de foie de morue	cod liver oil
huile *f* d'onagre	evening primrose oil
huile *f* d'olive	olive oil
huile *f* de tournesol	sunflower oil
huile *f* de germe de blé	wheat germ oil
inhalateur *m*	inhaler
inhalateur *m* buccal	mouth inhaler
inhalateur *m* de poche	pocket-size inhaler
insuline *f*	insulin

À LA PHARMACIE

PRODUITS DE PHARMACIE

laxatif *m*	laxative
lingettes *fpl*	wipes
lotion *f* antipelliculaire	dandruff lotion
lotion *f* après soleil	after-sun lotion
lotion *f* calmante à la calamine	calamine lotion
manuel *m* de premiers soins	first aid manual
masque *m*	mask
masque *m* à oxygène	oxygen mask
médicament *m* vendu sans ordonnance	over-the-counter medicine
mouchoirs *mpl* en papier	tissues, paper handkerchiefs
œillère *f*	eyebath
onctueux/euse	smooth, creamy
ordonnance *f*	prescription
ouate *f*, coton *m*	cotton wool
ouate *f* hydrophile	absorbent cotton wool
ouate *f* chirurgicale	surgical cotton wool
bâtonnet *m* de coton	cotton bud
pansement *m*	dressing, bandage
pansement *m* adhésif, sparadrap *m*	adhesive plaster
pansement *m* compressif	compressive bandage
pansement *m* sec/humide	dressing dry/moist
papier *m* hygiénique, papier-toilette *m*	toilet paper
paracétamol *m*	paracetemol
pastille *f* pour la toux	cough lozenge/sweet
pastilles *fpl* pour la gorge	throat pastilles
patch *m* à la nicotine	nicotine patch
peigne *m*	comb
peigne *m* à poux	fine-toothed comb (for head lice)
pellicules *fpl*	dandruff
pessaire *m* , ovule *m*	pessary
pilule *f*	pill
pilule *f* contraceptive	contraceptive pill
pince *f* à échardes	tweezers

À LA PHARMACIE

PRODUITS DE PHARMACIE

pince *f* à ongles, coupe-ongles *m*	nail clippers
pommade *f* contre les brûlures	ointment for burns
pommade *f* antibiotique	antibiotic ointment
pommade *f* anti-infection	disinfecting/germicidal ointment
pommade *f* pour les lèvres, pommade *f* rosat	lip salve
poudre *f*	powder
poudre *f* dentifrice	tooth powder
premiers soins *mpl*	first aid
préservatif *m*	condom
produit *m* amincissant, produit *m* pour maigrir	slimming product
produit *m* antimoustique	mosqito repellent
produit *m* contre l'acné	anti-acne cream/lotion
protège-slip *m*	panty liner
purgation *f*, purgatif *m* , purge *f*	purgative
quinine *f*	quinine
savon *m*	soap
savon *m* pour bébés	baby's soap
savon *m* dermatologique	dermatological soap
savon *m* de Marseille	household soap
savon *m* liquide	liquid soap
savon *m* doux	mild soap
savon *m* parfumé	scented soap
savon *m* à barbe	shaving soap
savon *m* mou	soft soap
savon *m* de toilette	toilet soap
sédatif *m*	sedative
serviette *f* hygiénique	sanitary towel
shampooing *m* antipelliculaire	dandruff shampoo
sirop *m* pour la toux, sirop *m* antitussif, antitussif *m*	cough mixture/syrup
solution *f* de stérilisation	sterilizing solution
somnifère *m*	sleeping pill

À LA PHARMACIE

PRODUITS DE PHARMACIE

somnifère *m*	soporific
sparadrap *m* microporeux	microporous adhesive tape
spray *m* , bombe *f* aérosol	spray
bombe *f* à raser	can of shaving cream
stérilisateur *m*	sterilizer
talc *m*	talc, talcum powder, baby powder
tampons *mpl* hygiéniques	tampons
teinture *f*	tincture, dye
teinture *f* d'iode	tincture of iodine
tranquillisant *m* , calmant *m*	tranqilllizer
tricostéril *m*	sterile compress
trousse *f* d'urgence	first aid box
trousse *f* de premiers soins, trousse à premier secours	first aid kit
valériane *f*	valerian
vaporisateur *m* , vapo *m*	spray, atomizer (for inhalant, throat, nose)
vaporisateur *m* à parfum	perfume atomizer
vaseline ® *f*	vaseline ®
verrucide *m*	wart remover
vitamine *f*	vitamin
vitaminé	with added vitamins/vitamin enriched
comprimé *m* de vitamines	vitamin tablet/pill
vitamine *f* C	vitamin C

LES INSTRUCTIONS
INSTRUCTIONS

Avalez les comprimés avant/ après le repas le matin/le soir avec un verre d'eau	Take the tablets before/after meals in the morning/at night with a glass of water
Prenez deux comprimés par jour	Take two tablets a day
Prenez deux cuillerées à café/à soupe	Take two tea/tablespoonsfuls

À LA PHARMACIE

CHEZ LE DENTISTE
AT THE DENTIST

LE MALADE

THE PATIENT

Je voudrais un rendez-vous, s'il vous plaît
I should like an appointment, please

Aussitôt que possible
As soon as possible

C'est urgent
It is urgent

J'ai mal aux dents
I have toothache

La dent me fait beaucoup de douleur
My tooth is hurting very much

Les dentistes me font peur
I am afraid of dentists

Vous pouvez arrêter la douleur?
Can you stop the pain?

Est-ce qu'il faudra enlever la dent?
Will the tooth have to come out?

Est-ce que vous me donnerez de l'anesthésie?
Will you give me an anaesthetic?

J'ai besoin de la toilette
I need the toilet

J'ai mal au cœur, j'ai envie de vomir
I feel sick

Je me sens évanoui/e
I feel faint

Qu'est-ce que le choix de traitements?
What treatments are available?

Ça coûtera combien?
How much will it cost?

Ça fait combien?
How much is that?

Il me faut un reçu
I need a receipt

Le dentier s'est cassé. Pouvez-vous le réparer ?
My denture is broken Can you mend it?

LE DENTISTE

THE DENTIST

C'est quoi, le problème?
What is the problem?

Pouvez-vous revenir plus tard/ demain?
Can you come back later/ tomorrow?

CHEZ LE DENTISTE

CHEZ LE DENTISTE

LE DENTISTE	THE DENTIST
Installez-vous ici	Sit here
Ouvrez bien la bouche	Open your mouth wide
Rincez-vous bien	Rinse well
N'essayez pas d'avaler	Don't try to swallow
Respirez lentement	Breathe slowly
Mordez fort	Bite hard
Il faut attendre quelques moments	We shall have to wait a few minutes
Il vous faut du plombage	You need a filling
Je vais essayer de sauver la dent	I shall try to save the tooth
Désolé mais il faut l'enlever	Sorry but it will have to come out
Il faut prendre une impression pour la couronne/la prothèse	I need to take an impression for the crown/denture
Il faut prendre une radio	I need to take an X-ray
Restez absolument tranquille	Stay absolutely still
Il vous faut un appareil orthodontique	You need a brace
Ce n'est que temporaire. Il faut consulter votre propre dentiste en rentrant	This is only temporary. You must visit your own dentist when you get back
Je vous donnerai une ordonnance pour la pharmacie	I shall give you a prescription for the chemist
Ça va pour aujourd'hui mais il faut un rendez-vous pour…	That's all for today but I need to see you again in…

VOCABULAIRE SUPPLÉMENTAIRE

abcès *m*	abscess
anesthésie *f*	anaesthesia
appareil *m* orthodontique	brace
appareil *m* rotatif à grande vitesse	high-speed drill
avaler	swallow to
bactéries *fpl*	bacteria
bain *m* de bouche	mouthwash
bouche *f*	mouth
bridge *m*	bridge
brossage *m*	brushing
brosse *f* à dents	toothbrush
brosse *f* à dents électrique	electric toothbrush
brosser	brush to
cabinet *m* dentaire	dental surgery
canal *m* des racines	root canal
carie *m* dentaire	caries, tooth decay
couronne *f*	crown
dent *f*	tooth
dent *f* de lait	milk tooth
dent *f* de sagesse	wisdom tooth
dent *f* définitive	permanent tooth
dentifrice *f*	toothpaste
dentiste *m* /*f*	dentist
dents *fpl* mal alignées	irregular teeth
détartrage *m*	scale
échographie *f*	scan
émail *f*	enamel
extraction *f*	extraction
feuille *f*	form
fil *m* dentaire	dental floss
fluorure *m*	fluoride
gencive *f*	gum
gingivite *f*	gingivitis

CHEZ LE DENTISTE

VOCABULAIRE SUPPLÉMENTAIRE

hypersensible	hypersensitive
inflammation *f*	inflammation
injection *f*	injection
mâchoire	jaw
mal *m* de dents	toothache
mastiquer	chew
mauvaise haleine *f*	halitosis/bad breath
mécanicien-dentiste *m*	dental technician
mordre	bite to
nerf *m*	nerve
orthodontiste *m* /f*	orthodontist
plaque *f* dentaire	plaque
plombage *m*	filling
polissage *m*	polish
prévention *f*	prevention
prise de sang *f*	blood test
prothèse *f* dentaire/ dentier *m*	denture
pyorrhée *f* avéolaire	pyorrhea
racine *f*	root
saignement *m*	bleeding
salive *f*	saliva
santé *f* bucco-dentaire	dental health
se carier	decay to
se laver les dents	clean one's teeth, to
soigner	look after, to
soins *mpl* conservation dents	check-up
ulcère *m*	ulcer

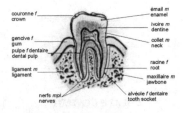

couronne *f* / crown
émail *m* / enamel
ivoire *m* / dentine
gencive *f* / gum
collet *m* / neck
pulpe *f* dentaire / dental pulp
ligament *m* / ligament
racine *f* / root
maxillaire *m* / jawbone
nerfs *mpl* / nerves
alvéole *f* dentaire / tooth socket

CHEZ L'OPTICIEN
AT THE OPTICIAN

L'OPTICIEN	**THE OPTICIAN**
Installez-vous par ici, s'il vous plaît	Sit down here, please
Enlevez les lunettes	Take off your glasses
Je voudrais faire un examen de vos lunettes	I'd like a look at your glasses
Est-ce que vous souffrez de maux de tête?	Do you suffer from headaches?
Il faut vous mettre des gouttes dans les yeux	I need to put some drops in your eyes
Patientez-vous ici pendant quelques minutes	Please wait here for a few minutes
Restez le menton ici	Put your chin on here
Dîtes-moi quand vous voyez la lumière	Tell me when you see a light
Vous pouvez lire quoi?	What can you read?
Vous pouvez lire ça?	Can you read this?
Vous pouvez lire jusqu'à où?	How far can you read?
Est-ce que ça va mieux que ça?	Is this better than this?
Lequel va mieux, le premier où le deuxième ?	Which is better, the first or the second?
Votre vue s'est améliorée/ détériorée	Your eyesight has improved/ deteriorated
Il y a un problème avec…	There is a problem with…
Je vous donnerai une ordonnance	I shall give you a prescription
Est-ce que vous avez votre ordonnance?	Do you have your prescription?
Voudriez-vous de nouvelle monture?	Would you like some new frames?
Vous gardez la monture?	Are you keeping these frames?

CHEZ L'OPTICIEN

CHEZ L'OPTICIEN

L'OPTICIEN

Vous avez choisi laquelle?
Elle sera prêt…
Je voudrais m'assurer que tout
  va bien

THE OPTICIAN

Which have you chosen?
They will be ready in…
I want to check they fit properly

LE MALADE

Les lunettes sont cassées. Vous
  pouvez les réparer?
Un verre s'est tombé de mes
  lunettes
Resserrez la vis s'il vous plaît

Il me faut des lunettes pour lire
Je voudrais un rendez-vous pour
  un examen de vue
Le dernier examen s'est passé…
Voici ma dernière ordonnance
Je souffre de maux de tête
J'ai des troubles de la vue
J'ai des troubles de vue en lisant
Je ne peux lire que la première
  ligne
Je peux lire jusqu'à…
Je porte des lunettes depuis…
Je crois qu'il me faut de lunettes
Seulement pour lire
Je voudrais essayer de lentilles
Je voudrais de lunettes de soleil
Il faut combien de temps?
C'est combien?
J'aime bien cette monture
Il ne faut que remplacer les
  verres

THE PATIENT

My glasses have broken. Can
  you mend them?
A lens has fallen out of my
  glasses
Can you tighten the screw
  please?
I need a pair of reading glasses
I should like an appointment for
  an eye test
My last test was…
This is my last prescription
I suffer from headaches
I'm having sight problems
I have difficulty seeing to read
I can only read the top line

I can read as far as…
I have worn glasses since/for …
I think I need glasses
For reading only
I should like to try contact lenses
I should like some sunglasses
How long will it take?
How much will it cost?
I really like these frames
I only want the lenses replacing

VOCABULAIRE SUPPLÉMENTAIRE

anti-choc	shock-resistant
antireflet/e	antireflective
arête *f*	bridge (of the nose)
astigmatisme *m*	astigmatism
bifocal/le	bifocal
cataracte *f*	cataract
cécité *f*	blindness
confortable	comfortable
conjonctivite *f*	conjunctivitis
cornée *f*	cornea
correction *f*	correction
cristallin *m*	lens (of the eye)
daltonisme *m*	colour blindness
décollement *m* de la rétine	detached retina
diabète *m*	diabetes
droit/e	right
dyslexie *f*	dyslexia
examen *m* de la vue	eye test
gauche	left
glaucome *m*	glaucoma
globe *m* oculaire	eyeball
gouttes *fpl*	drops
greffe *f* cornéenne	corneal graft
héméralopie *f*	night blindness
hypermétropie *f*	long sight
inconfortable, peu confortable	uncomfortable
inflammation *f*	inflammation *f*
iris *m*	iris
léger/ère	light (weight)
lentille *f* cornéenne, dure/souple	contact lens, hard/soft
lire	read to
louché/e	cross-eyed
lourd/e	heavy
lunettes *fpl* pour lire	reading glasses

CHEZ L'OPTICIEN

VOCABULAIRE SUPPLÉMENTAIRE

lunettes *fpl* de soleil	sunglasses
monture *f*	frames
myopie *f*	myopia
myopie *f*	short sight
nystagmus *m*	nystagmus
œil *m*	eye
ophtalmologiste *m*	ophthalmologist
ordonnance *f*	prescription
orgelet *m*	stye
paupière *f*	eyelid
progressif/ve	varifocal
resserrer	tighten to
rétine *f*	retina
sourcil *m*	eyelash
strabisme *m*	squint
verre *m*	lens (glass)
vis *f*	screw
vision *f* double	double vision

Dans le Royaume Uni, on peut demander un examen de vue chez l'opticien. Il existe des ophtalmologistes mais, d'habitude, on les consulte pour les troubles de vue plus spécialisées. Pour la plupart des gens, il faut payer pour un examen

CHEZ L'OPTICIEN

À L'HÔPITAL – COMME MALADE
IN HOSPITAL – AS A PATIENT

PHRASES UTILES	USEFUL EXPRESSIONS
Parlez-vous français?	Do you speak French?
Est-ce qu'il y a quelqu'un qui parle français?	Does anyone speak French?
Parlez plus lentement, s'il vous plaît	Please speak more slowly
Je ne comprends pas	I don't understand
Qu'est-ce que ça veut dire?	What does that mean?
Qu'est-ce que ce mot veut dire?	What does that word mean?
J'ai un rendez-vous avec/à…	I have an appointment with/at…
Je n'ai pas d'assurance maladie. Je vais payer moi-même	I don't have health insurance. I shall pay myself
C'est combien?	How much is that?
Il me faut un reçu, s'il vous plaît	I need a receipt please
Comment voudriez-vous régler?	How would you like to pay?
Je voudrais régler en espèces/ par carte bancaire/par chèque	I'd like to pay in cash/by credit card/by cheque
J'ai une carte Européenne d'Assurance Maladie	I have a European Health Insurance card
Puis-je vous aider?	Can I help you
Est-ce que vous pouvez m'aider?	Can you help me?
Qu'est-ce qu'il y a?	What is the matter?
J'ai un problème avec…	I have a problem with…
Je voudrais des renseignements sur…	I'd like some information about…
J'ai besoin de, il me faut	I need…
Qu'est-ce qui se passe?	What's happening?
Je ne sais pas	I don't know
Comment vous appelez-vous?/ Votre nom?	What is your name?

LE MALADE	**THE PATIENT**
Je m'appelle…/Mon nom est…	My name is…
La date de naissance, c'est quand?	What is your date of birth?
Comment ça va aujourd'hui?	How are you today?
Qu'est-ce qu'il a?	What is the matter?
Où ça vous fait mal?	Where does it hurt?
C'est arrivé quand?	When did this happen?
Comment c'est arrivé?	How did this happen ?
Je voudrais faire un examen/de votre …	I want to examine you/your …
Déshabillez-vous, s'il vous plaît	Get undressed please
Laissez votre/vos…	Leave on your…
Enlevez votre/vos…	Take off your….
Avez-vous des traitements en cours?	Are you on any medication?
Êtes-vous allergique à… ?	Are you allergic to…?
Il vous faut une prise de sang	You need a blood test
Il faudrait enlever les sutures dans…	The stitches will need to come out in ….
Je vous donnerai une ordonnance	I shall give you a prescription
Vous êtes fumeur?	Do you smoke?
Je ne me sens pas bien	I don't feel well
Je m'inquiète parce que…	I'm worried because…
Je me sens très faible	I feel very weak
Le/la…me fait mal	My…hurts/aches
J'ai mal au /à la…	I have a pain in my…
J'ai mal au cœur/ J'ai des nausées	I feel sick
J'ai/j'ai trouvé une grosseur	I have/I've found a lump
Je suis cardiaque	I have a heart condition
J'ai un stimulateur cardiaque	I have a pacemaker
Je fais de l'asthme	I am asthmatic
Je suis sous antibiotiques	I'm on antibiotics
J'ai un inhalateur	I have an inhaler
J'ai la diarrhée	I have diarrhoea

À L'HÔPITAL – COMME MALADE

LE MALADE	THE PATIENT
Je suis constipé/e	I am constipated
Je veux rentrer à la maison	I want to go home
Il faut rester en observation	I need to keep you in for observation
Il faut opérer	I need to operate
Vous pourriez rentrer aujourd'hui /demain/en quelques jours	You can go home today/ tomorrow/in a few days
Il vous faut un rendez-vous pour la semaine prochaine/dans un mois/dans six mois/dans une année	I need to see you again next week/next month/in six months/ in a year
Un autre rendez-vous n'est pas nécessaire	I don't need to see you again
Je vous donnerai une lettre pour votre généraliste	I shall give you a letter for your GP

VOCABULAIRE SUPPLÉMENTAIRE

accueil *m*	reception
ambulance *f*	ambulance
anesthésie *f*	anaesthesia
locale	local
générale	general
péridurale/épidurale	epidural
assurance *f* maladie	health/medical insurance
blessure *f*	wound
boisson *f*	drink
brûlure *f*	burn
cabinet *m*	consulting room
cabinet *m*	surgery (place)
cassé/e	broken
chaud/e	hot

À L'HÔPITAL – COMME MALADE

VOCABULAIRE SUPPLÉMENTAIRE

chirurgie *f*	surgery (operation)
choc *m*	shock
contusion *f*	bruise
décédé/e	dead
désinfecter	disinfect to
dossier *m*	file
échantillon *m*	specimen (urine/blood, tissue)
entorse *f*	sprain
examen *m*	examination
facture *f*	bill
fauteuil *m* roulant	wheelchair
fracturé/e	fractured
frissonner	shiver to
froid/e	cold
gelule *f*	capsule
goutte à goutte *f*	drip
guérir	cure to
heures *fpl* de visite	visiting hours
incision *f*	cut
inhalateur *m*	inhaler
inhaler	inhale
injection *f*	injection
intraveineux/euse	intravenous
lit *m*	bed
maternité *f*	maternity hospital
médicament *m*	medicine
médication *f*	medication
nettoyer	clean to
observation *f*	observation
opération *f*	operation
ordonnance *f*	prescription
oxygène *m*	oxygen
pansement *m*	bandage
pansement *m*	dressing
pansement *m* adhésif	plaster, adhesive (dressing)

À L'HÔPITAL – COMME MALADE

VOCABULAIRE SUPPLÉMENTAIRE

payer	pay (to)
percé/e	punctured
perfusion *f* sanguine	blood transfusion
pessaire *m*	pessary
pilule *f*	pill
plâtre *m*	plaster (for break/fracture)
pouls *m*	pulse
prélèvement *m*	specimen (blood, tissue)
prise de sang *f*	blood test
propre	clean
pus *m*	pus
radiographie *f*	x-ray
réanimation *f*	resuscitation
remède *m*	cure
rendez-vous *m*	appointment
renseignements *mpl*	information
renvoyer de l'hôpital	discharge to
repas *m*	food/meal
repos *m*	rest
s'infecter	infected to be
saignement *m*	bleeding
sale	dirty
service *m* de réanimation	intensive care
soins *m* pl coronariens	coronary care
sonde *f*	catheter
stéthoscope *m*	stethoscope
suppositoire *m*	suppository
surveillance *f*	monitoring
suture *f*	stitch
tension *f* (artérielle)	blood pressure
traitement *m*	treatment
urgences *fpl*	accident and emergency

À L'HÔPITAL – COMME MALADE

LES PRATICIENS	PRACTITIONERS
acupuncteur/euse	acupuncturist
anesthésiste	anaesthetist
auxiliaire médical	paramedic
cardiologue	cardiologist
chirurgien/ienne	surgeon
conseiller/ère	counsellor
dentiste	dentist
diététicien/ienne	dietician
docteur; médecin	doctor
ergothérapeute	occupational therapist
gastro-entérologue	gastro-enterologist
généraliste	general practitioner - GP
gérontologue	geriatrician
gynécologue	gynaecologist
herboriste	herbalist
homéopathe	homeopath
infirmier *m* en chef	charge nurse
infirmier/ière	nurse
médecin d'hôpital	hospital doctor
oncologiste	oncologist
ophtalmologiste	ophthalmologist
orthopédiste	orthopaedic
orthophoniste	speech therapist
oto-rhino-laryngologiste	ear, nose and throat
pédiatre	paediatrician
pédicure	chiropodist
pharmacien/ienne	chemist
physiothérapeute	physiotherapist
psychiatre	psychiatrist
psychologue	psychologist
radiologue	radiographer
réflexologiste	reflexologist
spécialiste	consultant; specialist
urologue	urologist

À L'HÔPITAL – COMME MALADE

À L'HÔPITAL - COMME VISITEUR
AT HOSPITAL – AS A VISITOR

PHRASES UTILES	USEFUL EXPRESSIONS
Excusez-moi	Excuse me
Où se trouve… ?	Where will I find…?
Il/elle est admis/e ce matin/ aujourd'hui/la nuit dernière/hier	He/she was admitted this morning/today/last night/ yesterday
Où se trouve l'unité… ?	Where is ward…?
Puis-je prendre l'ascenseur?	Can I use the lifts?
Les heures de visite sont quand?	What are the visiting hours?
Je cherche quelque chose à manger/à boire	Can I get something to eat/to drink?
Je reviendrai plus tard?	Shall I come back later?
Il/elle pourrait rentrer à la maison quand?	When can s/he go home?
Je voudrais le discuter avec quelqu'un	I'd like to talk to someone about it
C'est grave?	Is it serious?
Il/elle va récupérer?	Will he/she recover?
Je suis son mari/sa femme/sa mère/son père/son fils/sa fille/ son ami/e	I am her/his husband/wife/mother/father/son/ daughter/friend
Puis-je vous aider?	Can I help you?
Est-ce que vous pouvez m'aider ?	Can you help me?
Je voudrais des renseignements sur…	I'd like some information about…
Je cherche…	I am looking for…
Tournez à droite/à gauche	Turn right/left
Tout droit	Straight on

PHRASES UTILES	USEFUL EXPRESSIONS
Défense de fumer	No smoking
Je suis désolé/e	I am very sorry
Oui	Yes
Non	No

VOCABULAIRE SUPPLÉMENTAIRE

accueil *m*	reception
ascenseur *m*	lift, elevator
au revoir	goodbye
bonjour	good morning
bonsoir	good evening
chaise *f*	chair
couloir *m*	corridor
docteur *m* , médecin *m*	doctor
fermé	closed
grave	serious
heures *fpl* de visite	visiting hours
madame	madam
merci	thank you
monsieur	sir
numéros – impairs, pairs	numbers – odd, even
ouvert	open
pardon, excusez-moi	sorry
porte *f*	door
réanimation *f*	intensive care
renseignements *mpl*	information
s'il vous plaît	please
salle *f* d'attente	waiting room
service *m* , salle *f* d'hôpital, unité *f*	ward
service de maternité	maternity ward
service de pédiatrie	paediatric ward

À L'HÔPITAL - COMME VISITEUR

VOCABULAIRE SUPPLÉMENTAIRE

spécialiste *m*	specialist
toilettes *fpl*	toilets
messieurs, hommes	gents
femmes	ladies
handicapés	disabled
occupé	occupied
libre	free
urgences *fpl*	A & E

ACCIDENTS ET URGENCES
ACCIDENTS AND EMERGENCIES

DES PHRASES UTILES

USEFUL PHRASES

Au secours!	Help!
Aidez-moi s'il vous plaît	Help me please
Est-ce qu'il y a quelqu'un qui parle français?	Does anyone speak French?
Un accident est arrivé	There has been an accident
Il y a un incendie	There is a fire
Attention!	Watch out!
Téléphonez à la police/aux pompiers/à SAMU	Telephone the police/fire brigade/ambulance
Est-ce que vous avez un portable?	Do you have a mobile phone?
Il/elle est encore en vie	He/she is still breathing
Ce qui est arrivé c'est	This is what happened
Est-ce qu'il y a un docteur tout près?	Is there a doctor nearby?
Il y a une trousse de premiers soins dans la voiture	I have a First Aid kit in the car

ACCIDENTS ET URGENCES

ACCIDENTS ET URGENCES

Il/elle est sans connaissance	He/she is unconscious
Ne le/la bougez pas	Don't move him/her
Tenez-vous tranquille	Keep still
Vous avez quelque chose pour le/la couvrir?	Do you have something to cover him/her?
Il/elle est en un état de choc	He/she is in shock
Il/elle a fait une chute	He/she has fallen
Il/elle saigne du/de la	He/she is bleeding from
Je vais bien, merci	I'm OK, thank you
Je ne suis pas blessé/e	I'm not hurt

VOCABULAIRE SUPPLÉMENTAIRE

accident *m*	accident
accident *m* de la route	road accident
ambulance *f*	ambulance
blessé/e	injured/wounded
bouée *f* de sauvetage	lifebelt
brûlure *f*	burn
camion *m*	lorry
cassé/e	broken
chute *f*	fall
ciseaux *mpl*	scissors
coupure *f*	cut
désinfectant *m*	disinfectant
docteur *m* , médecin *m*	doctor
ébouillanté/e	scalded
en flammes	on fire
évanouir	faint (to)
faire mal (se)	hurt oneself (to)
glisser	slip (to)
incendie *f*	fire

ACCIDENTS ET URGENCES

VOCABULAIRE SUPPLÉMENTAIRE

lingette *f* antiseptique	antiseptic wipe
mort/e, décédé/e	dead
noyer (se)	drown (to)
pansement *m*	bandage
pansement *m* adhésif, sparadrap *m*	elastoplast ®
poison *m*	poison
police *f*	police
police secours *f*	emergency services
pompiers *mpl*	fire brigade
portable *m*	mobile phone
premier secours *mpl*	first aid
respirer	breathe (to)
SAMU (Service d'assistance médicale d'urgence)	emergency ambulance services
sans connaissance	unconscious
téléphone *m*	telephone
téléphoner	telephone (to)
tomber	fall (to)
trousse *f* de premiers soins	first aid kit
urgence *f*	emergency
voiture *f*	car

AU SECOURS !

Le numéro d'urgences c'est 999, par téléphone ou par portable. On vous demanderait quel service il vous faut, soit la police, les pompiers, l'ambulance ou la gendarmerie maritime. S'il vous en faut plusieurs, dîtes-le.

ACCIDENTS ET URGENCES

LE DÉCÈS

S'il arrive que quelqu'un meure dans le Royaume-Uni, il faut d'abord chercher un docteur. Le docteur délivrerait le certificat de décès (death certificate). Il en faudrait présenter une copie aux Pompes funèbres (undertakers) avant d'arranger les funerailles et puis au bureau de l'état civil (Registrar's Office) pour enregistrer le décès.

L'incinération est plus commun dans le Royaume-Uni qu'en France

L'ambassade ou le consulat français vous aidera à obtenir un certificat de décès, à organiser les funerailles où le rapatriement du corps.

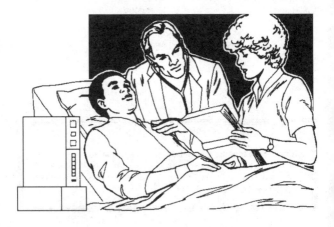

ACCIDENTS ET URGENCES

LES BESOINS DE BÉBÉ

absorber *v*	absorb (to)
alimentation infantile *f*	baby food
anneau *m* de dentition	teething ring
araser	level (to)
baignoire à bébé *f*	baby bath
barrière *f* de sécurité	staircase
bâtonnet *m* à coton	cotton bud
bavoir *m*	bib
biberon *m*	feeding bottle
bio	organic
biscuit *m* pour bébés	rusk
cache-prise *m*	plug cover
calmant *m* pour coliques infantiles	gripe water
caoutchouc *m*	rubber
couche *f*	nappy
cuillère *f*	spoon
cuillère *f* rase	level spoonful
dosette *f*	measure
drap *m*	towel
eau *f* nettoyante	cleanser
écoute-bébé *f*	baby alarm
gant *m* de toilette	flannel/face cloth
housse *f* de matelas	mattress cover
jouet *m*	toy

LES BESOINS DE BÉBÉ

lait *m* de toilette pour bébés	baby lotion
lait *m* infantile	baby milk
lait *m* maternel	breast milk
lingettes *fpl*	wipes
lit *m* à barreaux	cot
matelas *m*	mattress
matelas *m* à langer	changing mat
petit pot *m*	jar of baby food
plastique	plastic
porte-bébé *m*	baby carrier
pot *m*	potty
poussette *f*	pushchair
sans parfum	unperfumed
savon *m*	soap
shampooing *m*	shampoo
siège-auto *m*	car seat
stérilisateur *m*	sterilizer
stériliser	sterilize (to)
sucette *f*	dummy
table *f* à langer	changing table
talc *m*	talcum powder
tétine *f*	teat
vitamine *f*	vitamin

LES MALADIES COURANTES

abcès *m*	abscess
acné *f*	acne
acouphène *m*	tinnitus
alcoolisme *m*	alcoholism
allergie *f*	allergy
amnésie *f*	amnesia

RÉFÉRENCE

LES MALADIES COURANTES

anémie *f*	anaemia
anévrisme *m*	aneurism
angine *f*	angina
angine *f*	tonsillitis
anorexie *f*	anorexia
anxiété *f*	anxiety
appendicite *f*	appendicitis
arrêt *m* du cœur	heart failure
arthrite *f*	arthritis
asthme *m*	asthma
attaque cérébrale *f*	stroke
autisme *m*	autism
bec de lièvre *m*	hare lip
bouton *m* de fièvre	cold sore
bronchite *f*	bronchitis
brûlures *fpl* de l'estomac	heartburn
calcul biliaire *m*	gallstone
calcul rénal *m*	kidney stone
cancer *m*	cancer
cancer *m* de la prostate	prostate cancer
catarrhe *m*	catarrh
cécité *f*	blindness
choc *m*	shock
choc *m* anaphylactique	anaphylactic shock
cirrhose *f*	cirrhosis
coelialgie *f*	coeliac disease
colique *f*	colic
colite *f*	colitis
colostomie *f*	colostomy
coma *m*	coma
commotion *f* cérébrale	concussion
conjonctivite *f*	conjunctivitis
constipation *f*	constipation
convulsion *f*	convulsion
coqueluche *f*	whooping cough

RÉFÉRENCE

LES MALADIES COURANTES

coup de soleil *m*	sunburn
crampe *f*	cramp
croup *m*	croup
cystite *f*	cystitis
délire *f*	delirium
dépendance *f*	addiction
dépression *f*	depression
dermatite *f*	dermatitis
déshydration *f*	dehydration
diabète *m*	diabetes
diarrhée *f*	diarrhoea
diphtérie *f*	diphtheria
douleurs *fpl* de poitrine	chest pains
dyspepsie *f*, indigestion *f*	indigestion
dystrophie *f* musculaire	muscular dystrophy
eczéma *m*	eczema
embolie *f*	embolism
empoisonnement *m*	poisoning
encéphalite *f*	encephalitis
épilepsie *f*	epilepsy
éruption *f*	rash
fièvre *f*	fever
flatulence *f*	flatulence/wind
gale *f*	scabies
gastro-entérite *f*	gastroenteritis
goutte *f*	gout
grippe *f*	flu
hémophilie *f*	haemophilia
hémorragie *f*	haemorrhage
hémorragie *f* cérébrale	cerebral haemorrhage
hémorroïdes *fpl*	haemorrhoids
hépatite *f*	hepatitis
hernie *f*	hernia
hernie *f* locale	slipped disc
herpès *m*	herpes
hyperglycémie *f*	hyperglycaemia

RÉFÉRENCE

LES MALADIES COURANTES

hypertension *f* artérielle	hypertension
hyperthermie *f*	hyperthermia
hypoglycémie *f*	hypoglycaemia
impétigo *m*	impetigo
infarctus *m*	coronary thrombosis
intoxication *f* alimentaire	food poisoning
jaunisse *f*	jaundice
kyste *m*	cyst
la grippe	influenza
laryngite *f*	laryngitis
leucémie *f*	leukaemia
mal de tête *m*	headache
mal *m* à l'oreille	earache
mal *m* au dos	backache
maladie de cœur *f*	heart disease
maladie *f* de Parkinson	Parkinson's disease
maladie *f* d'Alzheimer	Alzheimer's disease
maladie *f* pulmonaire	pulmonary disease
mélanome *m*	melanoma
méningite *f*	meningitis
migraine *f*	migraine
mononucléose *f* infectieuse	glandular fever
muguet *m*	thrush
mycose *f*	athlete's foot
nausée *f*	nausea
oreillons *mpl*	mumps
ostéoarthrite *f*	osteoarthritis
otite *f*	ear infection
palais fendu *m*	cleft palate
paralysie *f*	paralysis
paralysie *f* cérébrale	cerebral palsy
paraplégie *f*	paraplegia
péritonite *f*	peritonitis
phobie *f*	phobia
pleurésie *f*	pleurisy

RÉFÉRENCE

LES MALADIES COURANT

pneumonie *f*	pneumonia
polio *f*	polio
polype *m*	polyp
refroidissement *m*	chill
rhume *m*	cold
rhume *m* des foins	hay fever
rubéole *f*	German measles
rugéole *f*	measles
saignement *m* de nez	nosebleed
scarlatine *f*	scarlet fever
schizophrénie *f*	schizophrenia
sciatique *f*	sciatica
sclérose *f* en plaques	multiple sclerosis
sinusite *f*	sinusitis
spina-bifida *m*	spina bifida
stress *m*	stress
surdité *f*	deafness
syndrome *m* de Down	Down syndrome
tétanos *m*	tetanus
thrombose *f*	thrombosis
toux *f*	cough
tuberculose *f*	tuberculosis
ulcère *m*	ulcer
ulcère *m* de l'estomac	gastric ulcer
urticaire *f*	urticaria
varicelle *f*	chicken pox
varices *f*pl	varicose veins
vertige *m*	dizziness
vertige *m*	vertigo
virus *m*	virus

LE CORPS

abdomen *m*, ventre *m*	abdomen
aine *f*	groin
aisselle *f*	armpit
anus *m*	anus
appendice *m*	appendix
artère *f*	artery
bassin *m*	pelvis
bouche *f*	mouth
bras *m*	arm
cage thoracique *f*	ribcage
cartilage *m*	cartilage
cerveau *m*	brain
cheville *f*	ankle
cil *m*	eyelash
clavicule *f*	collarbone
coccyx *m*	coccyx
cœur *m*	heart
colon *m*	colon
colonne vertébrale *f*	spine
côte *f*	rib
cou *m*	neck
coude *m*	elbow
crâne *m*	skull
cuisse *f*	thigh
dent *f*	tooth
diaphragme *m*	midriff
doigt *m*	finger
épaule *f*	shoulder
estomac *m* , ventre *m*	stomach
fémur *m*	thighbone
fesse *f*	buttock
foie *f*	liver
front *m*	forehead
genou *m*	knee
glande *f*	gland
gorge *f*	throat

hanche *f*

LE CORPS

intestin *m*	intestine
intestins *mpl*	bowel
jambe *f*	leg
joint à rotule *m*	ball and socket joint
joint *m*	joint
joue *f*	cheek
langue *f*	tongue
larynx *m*	larynx
lèvre *f*	lip
ligament *m*	ligament
mâchoire *f*	jaw
main *f*	hand
mamelon *m*	nipple
menton *m*	chin
moelle *f* épinière	spinal cord
mollet *m*	calf
muscle *m*	muscle
narine *f*	nostril
nerf *m*	nerve
nez *m*	nose
nombril *m*	navel
nuque *f*	nape
œil *m* /yeux *m pl*	eye/eyes
œsophage *m*	oesophagus
omoplate *f*	shoulder blade
ongle *m*	nail
oreille *f*	ear
orteil *m*	toe
os *m*	bone
pancréas *m*	pancreas
paupière *f*	eyelid
pénis *m*	penis
pied *m*	foot
poignet *m*	wrist

LE CORPS

poitrine *f*	chest
postérieur *m*	bottom
pouce *f*	thumb
poumon *m*	lung
pubis *m*	pubis
rate *f*	spleen
rectum *m*	rectum
rein *m*	kidney
rotule *f*	kneecap
sang *m*	blood
scrotum *m*	scrotum
sein *m*	breast
sinus *m*	sinus
sourcil *m*	eyebrow
squelette *m*	skeleton
sternum *m*	breastbone
talon *m*	heel
tempe *f*	temple
tendon *m*	tendon
tete	head
thyroïde *f*	thyroid
tibia *m*	shinbone
tonsille *f*	tonsil
trachée *f*	windpipe
utérus *m*	uterus
vagin *m*	vagina
valvule *f*	valve
végétations *fpl*	adenoids
veine *f*	vein
vertèbre *f*	vertebra
vésicule *f* biliaire	gall bladder
vessie *f*	bladder
visage *m*	face
vulve *f*	vulva

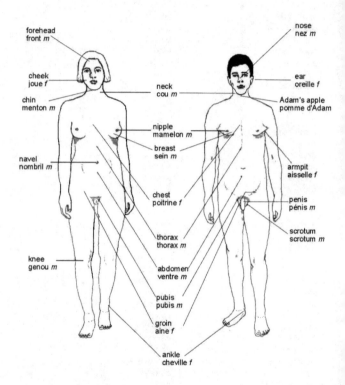

forehead
front *m*

cheek
joue *f*

chin
menton *m*

nose
nez *m*

ear
oreille *f*

neck
cou *m*

Adam's apple
pomme d'Adam

nipple
mamelon *m*

breast
sein *m*

navel
nombril *m*

armpit
aisselle *f*

chest
poitrine *f*

penis
pénis *m*

scrotum
scrotum *m*

thorax
thorax *m*

knee
genou *m*

abdomen
ventre *m*

pubis
pubis *m*

groin
aine *f*

ankle
cheville *f*

RÉFÉRENCE

LE CORPS

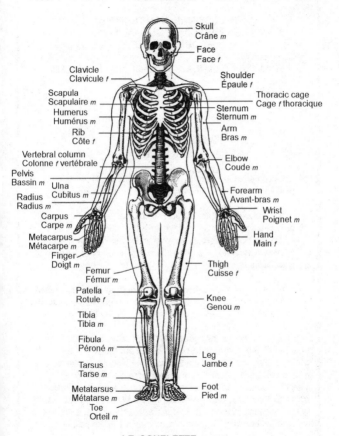

Skull
Crâne *m*

Face
Face *f*

Clavicle
Clavicule *f*

Shoulder
Épaule *f*

Scapula
Scapulaire *m*

Thoracic cage
Cage *f* thoracique

Humerus
Humérus *m*

Sternum
Sternum *m*

Rib
Côte *f*

Arm
Bras *m*

Vertebral column
Colonne *f* vertébrale

Elbow
Coude *m*

Pelvis
Bassin *m*

Ulna
Cubitus *m*

Forearm
Avant-bras *m*

Radius
Radius *m*

Wrist
Poignet *m*

Carpus
Carpe *m*

Hand
Main *f*

Metacarpus
Métacarpe *m*

Finger
Doigt *m*

Femur
Fémur *m*

Thigh
Cuisse *f*

Patella
Rotule *f*

Knee
Genou *m*

Tibia
Tibia *m*

Fibula
Péroné *m*

Leg
Jambe *f*

Tarsus
Tarse *m*

Foot
Pied *m*

Metatarsus
Métatarse *m*

Toe
Orteil *m*

LE SQUELETTE

GLOSSAIRE DES TERMES MÉDICAUX, DE SANTÉ ET DE PHARMACIE

FRANÇAIS – ANGLAIS et ANGLAIS - FRANÇAIS

par Alan S. Lindsey

livre de poche 204 pages, 210 x 148 mm
Publié 2003
ISBN 1-872739-12-1
Prix: £12.50

> Une compilation nouvelle fournissant plus de 3000 termes médicaux, de santé et de pharmacie en français et anglais.

> Le Glossaire inclut les maladies courantes, les termes anatomiques, les termes de premier soins et de l'hôpital, ainsi que les termes de pharmacie, comprenant les medicaments, les articles de toilette, les produits de beauté, de santé et les produits pharmaceutiques.

> Definitions aide-memoire en français et en anglais de beaucoup de termes médicaux. Un grand nombre d'expressions (françaises et anglaises) pour utiliser en la situation médicale.

La publication décrit au-dessus est disponible dans les libraries dans le UK par commande ou on peut l'obtenir directement de Hadley Pager Info par envoyant un chèque pour couvrir le prix (frais d'expédition inclus pour les adresses en UK, ajouter 10% si en l'Europe, ou 16% si hors de l'Europe) **à Hadley Pager Info, PO Box 249, Leatherhead, KT23 3WX, England**. Liste de Publications disponible de cette adresse, ou par e-courrier: **hpinfo@aol.com**   Website: **http:// www.hadleypager.com**